Measuring Up®

to the California Content Standards

English Language Arts

This book is customized for California and the lessons cover the California Content Standards. The Measuring Up® program includes instructional worktexts and Diagnostic Practice Tests, which are available separately.

Level B

800-822-1080
www.PeoplesEducation.com

Peoples Education®
Your partner in student success™

$ 200
7/19

Publisher: Diane Miller
Editorial Development: e2 Publishing Services
Acting Editorial Director: Eugene McCormick
Senior Editor: Scott Caffrey
Vice President of Production and Manufacturing:
Doreen Smith
Vice President of Marketing: Victoria Ameer Kiely
Director of Marketing: Melissa Dubno Geller
Pre-Press & Production Manager: Gerald Giordano
Project Manager: Jennifer Heart
Production Editor: Alexis Rodriguez
Copy Editors: Dee Josephson, Michele Wells
Proofreaders: Pat Smith, Josh Gillenson
Photo Researcher/Permissions Manager: Kristine Liebman
Illustrators: Armando Báez, Sal Esposito
Cover Design: Yadiro Henriquez, Cynthia Mackowicz,
   Michele Sakow

Advisory Panel, Elementary School:
Jack Reed, San Bernardino Unified School District,
   San Bernardino, CA
Debra A. Smith, Ernest R. Geddes Elementary School, Baldwin Park

Peoples Education
Your partner in student success™

Copyright © 2006
Peoples Education, Inc.
299 Market Street
Saddle Brook, New Jersey 07663

ISBN 978-1-4138-2331-8

Printed in the United States of America.

Manufactured in Ann Arbor, MI in January 2011 by Edwards Brothers, Inc.

30   29   28   27   26   25   24   23   22   21

Measuring Up®
Contents

Part 1: Vocabulary, Reading Comprehension, and Literature

Chapter 1 Word Analysis and Vocabulary Development

Lesson	California Content Standards Reading Vocabulary		

Chapter 1 Word Analysis and Vocabulary Development

Chapter 2 Reading Comprehension

Chapter 3 Literary Response and Analysis

Part 2: Writing

Chapter 4 Writing Conventions

Chapter 5 Writing Strategies and Applications

DPTs (Diagnostic Practice Tests) .... Measuring Up® Supplement

Your teacher may choose to give Diagnostic Practice Tests that assess your understanding of skills and concepts that come from your California Content Standards. This will help you focus on areas where you need some extra help.

Teachers: Refer to www.CAStandardsHelp.com for teaching strategies and ELL teaching activities.

Correlation to the California Content Standards

This worktext is customized to the California Content Standards.

The correlation chart shows how Measuring Up® is vertically aligned to the California Content Standards because the lessons are customized for them. As the lesson for each student expectation is completed, place a (✔) to indicate Mastery or an (✗) to indicate Review Needed.

Chapter 1: Word Analysis and Vocabulary Development	Master Skill						
	Review Skill						
	Lessons	1	2	3	4	5	B
California Content Standard 1.0—Word Analysis, Fluency, and Systematic Vocabulary Development Students understand the basic features of reading. They select letter patterns and know how to translate them into spoken language by using phonics, syllabication, and word parts. They apply this knowledge to achieve fluent oral and silent reading.							
2.1.1 Decoding and Word Recognition: Recognize and use knowledge of spelling patterns (e.g., diphthongs, special vowel spellings) when reading.		★	✓	✓	✓	✓	★
2.1.2 Decoding and Word Recognition: Apply knowledge of basic syllabication rules when reading (e.g., vowel-consonant-vowel = su/per; vowel-consonant/consonant-vowel = sup/per).		○	★	✓	✓	✓	★
2.1.3 Decoding and Word Recognition: Decode two-syllable nonsense words and regular multisyllable words.		○	○	★	✓	✓	★
2.1.4 Decoding and Word Recognition: Recognize common abbreviations (e.g., Jan., Sun., Mr., St.).		○	○	○	★	✓	★
2.1.5 Decoding and Word Recognition: Identify and correctly use regular plurals (e.g., -s, -es, -ies) and irregular plurals (e.g., fly/flies, wife/wives).		○	○	○	○	★	★

Chapter 1: Word Analysis and Vocabulary Development	Master Skill						
	Review Skill						
	Lessons	6	7	8	9	10	B
California Content Standard 1.0—Word Analysis, Fluency, and Systematic Vocabulary Development Students understand the basic features of reading. They select letter patterns and know how to translate them into spoken language by using phonics, syllabication, and word parts. They apply this knowledge to achieve fluent oral and silent reading.							
2.1.6 Decoding and Word Recognition: Read aloud fluently and accurately and with appropriate intonation and expression.		★	✓	✓	✓	✓	★
2.1.7 Vocabulary and Concept Development: Understand and explain common antonyms and synonyms.		○	★	✓	✓	✓	★
2.1.8 Vocabulary and Concept Development: Use knowledge of individual words in unknown compound words to predict their meaning.		○	○	★	✓	✓	★
2.1.9 Vocabulary and Concept Development: Know the meaning of simple prefixes and suffixes (e.g., over-, un-, -ing, -ly).		○	○	○	★	✓	★
2.1.10 Vocabulary and Concept Development: Identify simple multiple-meaning words.		○	○	○	○	★	★

★ **STANDARD COVERED**   ✓ **STANDARD PREVIOUSLY COVERED**

○ **STANDARD TO BE COVERED**   B **Building Stamina**®

Correlation to the California Content Standards

This worktext is customized to the California Content Standards.

The correlation chart shows how Measuring Up® is vertically aligned to the California Content Standards because the lessons are customized for them. As the lesson for each student expectation is completed, place a (✓) to indicate Mastery or an (✗) to indicate Review Needed.

		Master Skill										
Chapter 2: Reading Comprehension	Review Skill											
	Lessons	11	12	13	14	15	16	17	18	19	B
California Content Standard 2.0—Reading Comprehension: Students read and understand grade-level-appropriate material. They draw upon a variety of comprehension strategies as needed (e.g., generating and responding to essential questions, making predictions, comparing information from several sources). The selections in *Recommended Readings in Literature, Kindergarten Through Grade Eight* illustrate the quality and complexity of the materials to be read by students. In addition to their regular school reading, by grade four, students read one-half million words annually, including a good representation of grade-level-appropriate narrative and expository text (e.g., classic and contemporary literature, magazines, newspapers, online information). In grade two, students continue to make progress toward this goal.												
2.2.1	Structural Features of Informational Materials: Use titles, tables of contents, and chapter headings to locate information in expository text.	★	✓	✓	✓	✓	✓	✓	✓	✓	★
2.2.2	Comprehension and Analysis of Grade-Level-Appropriate Text: State the purpose in reading (i.e., tell what information is sought).	○	★	✓	✓	✓	✓	✓	✓	✓	★
2.2.3	Comprehension and Analysis of Grade-Level-Appropriate Text: Use knowledge of the author's purpose(s) to comprehend informational text.	○	○	★	✓	✓	✓	✓	✓	✓	★
2.2.4	Comprehension and Analysis of Grade-Level-Appropriate Text: Ask clarifying questions about essential textual elements of exposition (e.g., *why, what if, how*).	○	○	○	★	✓	✓	✓	✓	✓	★
2.2.5	Comprehension and Analysis of Grade-Level-Appropriate Text: Restate facts and details in the text to clarify and organize ideas.	○	○	○	○	★	✓	✓	✓	✓	★
2.2.6	Comprehension and Analysis of Grade-Level-Appropriate Text: Recognize cause-and-effect relationships in a text.	○	○	○	○	○	★	✓	✓	✓	★
2.2.7	Comprehension and Analysis of Grade-Level-Appropriate Text: Interpret information from diagrams, charts, and graphs.	○	○	○	○	○	○	★	✓	✓	★
2.2.8	Comprehension and Analysis of Grade-Level-Appropriate Text: Follow two-step written instructions.	○	○	○	○	○	○	○	★	✓	★

★ **STANDARD COVERED**   ✓ **STANDARD PREVIOUSLY COVERED**

○ **STANDARD TO BE COVERED**   B **Building Stamina®**

Correlation to the California Content Standards

This worktext is customized to the California Content Standards.

The correlation chart shows how Measuring Up® is vertically aligned to the California Content Standards because the lessons are customized for them. As the lesson for each student expectation is completed, place a (✓) to indicate Mastery or an (✗) to indicate Review Needed.

Chapter 3: Literary Response and Analysis

	Master Skill						
	Review Skill						
	Lessons	19	20	21	22	23	B

California Content Standard 3.0—Literary Response and Analysis Students read and respond to a wide variety of significant works of children's literature. They distinguish between the structural features of the text and the literary terms or elements (e.g., theme, plot, setting, characters). The selections in *Recommended Readings in Literature, Kindergarten Through Grade Eight* illustrate the quality and complexity of the materials to be read by students.

		19	20	21	22	23	B
2.3.1	Narrative Analysis of Grade-Level-Appropriate Text: Compare and contrast plots, settings, and characters presented by different authors.	★	★	★	✓	✓	★
2.3.2	Narrative Analysis of Grade-Level-Appropriate Text: Generate alternative endings to plots and identify the reason or reasons for, and the impact of, the alternatives.	★	✓	✓	✓	✓	★
2.3.3	Narrative Analysis of Grade-Level-Appropriate Text: Compare and contrast different versions of the same stories that reflect different cultures.	○	○	○	★	✓	★
2.3.4	Narrative Analysis of Grade-Level-Appropriate Text: Identify the use of rhythm, rhyme, and alliteration in poetry.	○	○	○	○	★	★

Chapter 4: Writing Conventions

	Master Skill							
	Review Skill							
	Lessons	24	25	26	27	28	29	30	B

California Content Standard 1.0—Written and Oral English Language Conventions: Students write and speak with a command of standard English conventions appropriate to this grade level.

		24	25	26	27	28	29	30	B
2.1.1	Sentence Structure: Distinguish between complete and incomplete sentences.	★	✓	✓	✓	✓	✓	✓	★
2.1.2	Sentence Structure: Recognize and use the correct word order in written sentences.	○	○	★	✓	✓	✓	✓	★
2.1.3	Grammar: Identify and correctly use various parts of speech, including nouns and verbs, in writing and speaking.	○	★	✓	✓	✓	✓	✓	★
2.1.4	Punctuation: Use commas in the greeting and closure of a letter and with dates and items in a series.	○	○	○	★	✓	✓	✓	★
2.1.5	Punctuation: Use quotation marks correctly.	○	○	○	○	★	✓	✓	★
2.1.6	Capitalization: Capitalize all proper nouns, words at the beginning of sentences and greetings, months and days of the week, and titles and initials of people.	○	○	○	○	○	★	✓	★
2.1.7	Spelling: Spell frequently used, irregular words correctly (e.g., *was, were, says, said, who, what, why*).	○	○	○	○	○	○	★	★
2.1.8	Spelling: Spell basic short-vowel, long-vowel, *r*-controlled, and consonant-blend patterns correctly.	○	○	○	○	○	○	★	★

★ **STANDARD COVERED** ✓ **STANDARD PREVIOUSLY COVERED**

○ **STANDARD TO BE COVERED** B **Building Stamina®**

Correlation to the California Content Standards

This worktext is customized to the California Content Standards.

The correlation chart shows how Measuring Up® is vertically aligned to the California Content Standards because the lessons are customized for them. As the lesson for each student expectation is completed, place a (✓) to indicate Mastery or an (✗) to indicate Review Needed.

Chapter 5: Writing Strategies and Applications

	Master Skill			
	Review Skill			
	Lessons	31	32	33	B

		31	32	33	B
California Content Standard 2.0—Writing Applications (Genres and Their Characteristics): Students write compositions that describe and explain familiar objects, events, and experiences. Student writing demonstrates a command of standard American English and the drafting, research, and organizational strategies outlined in Writing Standard 1.0. Using the writing strategies of grade two outlined in Writing Standard 1.0, students:					
2.2.1	Write brief narratives based on their experiences: **a.** Move through a logical sequence of events. **b.** Describe the setting, characters, objects, and events in detail.	★	✓	✓	★
2.2.2	Write a friendly letter complete with the date, salutation, body, closing, and signature.	○	★	✓	★
California Content Standard 1.0—Writing Strategies: Students write clear and coherent sentences and paragraphs that develop a central idea. Their writing shows they consider the audience and purpose. Students progress through the stages of the writing process (e.g., prewriting, drafting, revising, editing successive versions).					
2.1.1	Organization and Focus: Group related ideas and maintain a consistent focus.	★	★	✓	★
2.1.2	Penmanship: Create readable documents with legible handwriting.	★	★	✓	★
2.1.3	Research: Understand the purposes of various reference materials (e.g., dictionary, thesaurus, atlas).	○	○	★	★
California Content Standard 1.0—Written and Oral English Language Conventions: Students write and speak with a command of standard English conventions appropriate to this grade level.		★	★	✓	★
2.1.4	Punctuation: Use commas in the greeting and closure of a letter and with dates and items in a series.	○	★	✓	★

Research Handbook

	Master Skill	
	Review Skill	
	Lessons	

California Content Standard 1.0—Writing Strategies: Students write clear and coherent sentences and paragraphs that develop a central idea. Their writing shows they consider the audience and purpose. Students progress through the stages of the writing process (e.g., prewriting, drafting, revising, editing successive versions).		
3.1.3	Research: Understand the structure and organization of various reference materials (e.g., dictionary, thesaurus, atlas, encyclopedia).	★

★ **STANDARD COVERED**　　✓ **STANDARD PREVIOUSLY COVERED**

○ **STANDARD TO BE COVERED**　　B **Building Stamina**®

What's Inside: A Lesson Guide

Lessons in this worktext are divided into four sections in which individual content standards are introduced, explained, applied, and assessed.

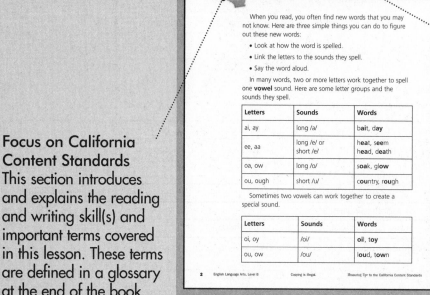

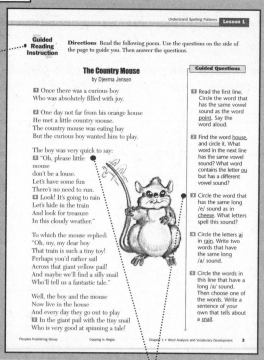

Focus on California Content Standards
This section introduces and explains the reading and writing skill(s) and important terms covered in this lesson. These terms are defined in a glossary at the end of the book.

Here are the California Content Standards on which this lesson focuses.

Guided Reading Instruction
Guided Reading and Guided Writing questions guide students and teachers in using the skills listed in the "Focus" section of the lesson. These questions may be answered through writing or discussion. Additional short-response questions follow the Guided Reading. These enable students to interact with the text through short written responses.

You can connect a numbered Guided Reading question or activity to the selection by looking for a box with the same number.

Apply
Read this second passage and answer the short-response questions that follow to apply the skills you have learned.

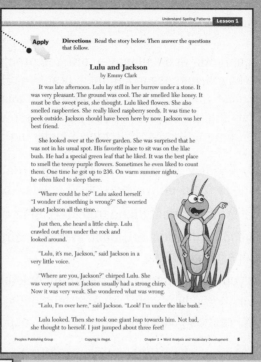

Apply **Directions** Read the story below. Then answer the questions that follow.

Lulu and Jackson
by Emmy Clark

It was late afternoon. Lulu lay still in her burrow under a stone. It was very pleasant. The ground was cool. The air smelled like honey. It must be the sweet peas, she thought. Lulu liked flowers. She also smelled raspberries. She really liked raspberry seeds. It was time to peek outside. Jackson should have been here by now. Jackson was her best friend.

She looked over at the flower garden. She was surprised that he was not in his usual spot. His favorite place to sit was on the lilac bush. He had a special green leaf that he liked. It was the best place to smell the teeny purple flowers. Sometimes he even liked to count them. One time he got up to 236. On warm summer nights, he often liked to sleep there.

"Where could he be?" Lulu asked herself. "I wonder if something is wrong?" She worried about Jackson all the time.

Just then, she heard a little chirp. Lulu crawled out from under the rock and looked around.

"Lulu, it's me, Jackson," said Jackson in a very little voice.

"Where are you, Jackson?" chirped Lulu. She was very upset now. Jackson usually had a strong chirp. Now it was very weak. She wondered what was wrong.

"Lulu, I'm over here," said Jackson. "Look! I'm under the lilac bush."

Lulu looked. Then she took one giant leap towards him. Not bad, she thought to herself. I just jumped about three feet!

Peoples Publishing Group   Copying is illegal.   Chapter 1 • Word Analysis and Vocabulary Development   **5**

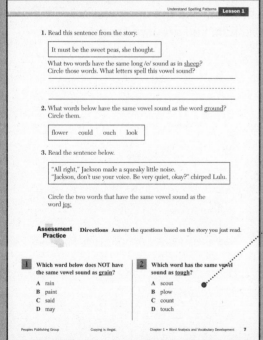

1. Read this sentence from the story.

> It must be the sweet peas, she thought.

What two words have the same long /e/ sound as in sheep? Circle those words. What letters spell this vowel sound?

_____

- -

2. What words below have the same vowel sound as the word ground? Circle them.

> flower   could   ouch   look

3. Read the sentence below.

> "All right," Jackson made a squeaky little noise.
> "Jackson, don't use your voice. Be very quiet, okay?" chirped Lulu.

Circle the two words that have the same vowel sound as the word joy.

Assessment Practice **Directions** Answer the questions based on the story you just read.

1 Which word below does NOT have the same vowel sound as grain?

A rain
B paint
C said
D may

2 Which word has the same vowel sound as tough?

A scout
B plow
C count
D touch

Peoples Publishing Group   Copying is illegal.   Chapter 1 • Word Analysis and Vocabulary Development   **7**

Assessment Practice
Answer these multiple-choice questions about the second passage—the one you read in the Apply section. The questions will test how well you have understood the skills in the lesson. Make sure you circle the letter of the correct answer choice for each question.

to the
California Content Standards

Dear Student,

How do you get better at anything you do? You practice! Just like with sports or other activities, the key to success in school is practice. The same goes for learning skills in the area of English language arts. The lessons in this Measuring Up book are geared to help you review and practice what you need to know for your grade level according to the California Content Standards established by the State of California.

Measuring Up has five chapters. The first three chapters focus on reading skills, and the next two chapters focus on writing skills. Each lesson consists of four main sections:

• **Focus on California Content Standards** introduces the skills covered in the lesson.

• **Guided Reading Instruction** or **Guided Writing Instruction** shows you the skills you will need for successful learning.

• **Apply** helps you comprehend important concepts and skills by reading passages and answering open-ended or short-answer questions.

• **Assessment Practice** gives you experience in responding to questions in test format.

In addition to the lessons, review sections in the book are called **Building Stamina**. They contain multiple-choice questions and writing prompts like the ones you will see on tests. Many of these are more difficult and will help you prepare for the harder questions.

Have a terrific year!

PEOPLES
PUBLISHING GROUP

to the
California Content Standards

To Parents and Families,

All students need reading and writing skills to succeed. California educators have created the California Content Standards for English Language Arts and have set the standards for reading and writing that all California students should meet at each grade level.

The California Content Standards emphasize higher-level thinking skills. Students must learn to think on a higher level, to consider, analyze, interpret, and evaluate instead of just recalling simple facts.

Measuring Up® will help your children to learn the California Content Standards and prepare for all English language arts exams. It contains:

• lessons that focus on practicing the California Content Standards;

• **Guided Reading Instruction,** in which shaded numbers in text correspond to questions in the margin that guide reading by highlighting particular skills;

• writing responses to varied reading selections;

• revision exercises and writing prompts;

• **Assessment Practice,** which shows how individual Content Standards can be understood through multiple-choice questions;

• **Building Stamina®,** which gives practice in uncovering themes in passages and answering multiple-choice questions that require higher-level thinking.

For success in school and the real world, your child needs good reading and writing skills. Get involved! Your involvement is crucial to your child's success. Here are some suggestions:

• Make sure your home shows that reading and writing are important. Keep bookshelves on display. Share stories from newspapers and magazines. Talk to librarians at the school or public library to find out what kids are reading.

• Treat reading as a pleasure, not a punishment. Give books as presents and show that you like to receive them, too. Respect each other's private reading time.

• Help to find appropriate Internet sites for literature, information, and reviews. Play recorded books together when riding in the car. Watch plays on television. Make a family outing of book signings and talks at your local library or bookstore.

• Encourage your child to write and talk about what he or she has written.

Work with us this year to ensure your child's success. Reading and writing are essential skills for success and pleasure throughout your child's life.

This book was built for California students like you! Every lesson, every question, and every selection is geared toward helping you master the California Content Standards and prepare for any rigorous exam you may be required to take in English language arts this year and in the future.

About the California Content Standards

California educators have created the California Content Standards for English Language Arts. These standards describe exactly what is expected of all students at each grade level. Lessons within this book are correlated to meet the following California Content Standards:

Reading Content Standards

1.0 Word Analysis, Fluency, and Systematic Vocabulary Development Students understand the basic features of reading. They select letter patterns and know how to translate them into spoken language by using phonics, syllabication, and word parts. They apply this knowledge to achieve fluent oral and silent reading.

2.0 Reading Comprehension Students read and understand grade-level-appropriate material. They draw upon a variety of comprehension strategies as needed (e.g., generating and responding to essential questions, making predictions, comparing information from several sources). The selections in *Recommended Readings in Literature, Kindergarten Through Grade Eight* illustrate the quality and complexity of the materials to be read by students. In addition to their regular school reading, by grade four, students read one-half million words annually, including a good representation of grade-level-appropriate narrative and expository text (e.g., classic and contemporary literature, magazines, newspapers, online information). In grade two, students make substantial progress toward this goal.

3.0 Literary Response and Analysis: Students read and respond to a wide variety of significant works of children's literature. They distinguish between the structural features of the text and the literary terms or elements (e.g., theme, plot, setting, characters). The selections in *Recommended Readings in Literature, Kindergarten Through Grade Eight* illustrate the quality and complexity of the materials to be read by students.

Writing Content Standards

1.0 Written and Oral English Language Conventions Students write and speak with a command of standard English conventions appropriate to this grade level.

1.0 Writing Strategies Students write clear and coherent sentences and paragraphs that develop a central idea. Their writing shows they consider the audience and purpose. Students progress through the stages of the writing process (e.g., prewriting, drafting, revising, editing successive versions).

2.0 Writing Applications (Genres and Their Characteristics) Students write compositions that describe and explain familiar objects, events, and experiences. Student writing demonstrates a command of standard American English and the drafting, research, and organizational strategies outlined in Writing Standard 1.0.

Measuring Up® on Multiple-Choice Questions

A multiple-choice question has two parts. The first part is the question, or stem. It has a number in front of it. The second part is the choices, or answers. Your job is to pick the one correct choice. Here are some tips for answering multiple-choice questions:

- Many questions refer to a specific paragraph in a selection. Go back and reread that paragraph to find the correct answer.
- Some multiple-choice questions may refer to an illustration that is shown with an informational passage. Look at the text and graphics and how they work together. Then try to answer the specific question.
- Remember that many harder questions test higher-order thinking skills. You will not find the exact answer right there in the passage. Instead, you have to connect ideas and information to come up with the right answers.
- Rule out the wrong answers. Even if you don't know the answer to a multiple-choice question, you may still be able to guess and get the question right. Rule out answers that you know are definitely wrong. If you can narrow the possibilities to two choices, you can guess and have a good chance of picking the correct answer.
- Check your answers. Before you turn in a test, reread each question and the choices to double-check that you have chosen the correct one. In addition, make sure you haven't marked a wrong choice by mistake.

There are different kinds of multiple-choice questions. One kind looks like this:

1 **At the END of both stories, Josie decides that**

    A winter is a fun time of year.

    B there are a lot of holidays during the winter.

    C winter is not as much fun as summer.

    D she doesn't like the winter.

To answer this type of question, choose the answer choice that best finishes the sentence.

Another kind looks like this:

2 **Which step tells you how much water to add?**

    A   Step 1

    B   Step 2

    C   Step 3

    D   Step 4

To answer this type of question, choose the best answer.

Another kind of multiple-choice question asks you to listen to the question. For example, a test administrator may read:

3 **Find the word that has the same sound as the underlined letter or letters in the first word.**

> scared

    A   scored

    B   shared

    C   snored

    D   snared

To answer this type of question, listen to the question. Then, think about the sound of the underlined letters. Then choose the answer that best fits that sound.

Getting a Head Start on Revising and Editing

On a test, the revising and editing part tests your ability to spot and correct trouble spots in a written passage. Here are some tips for responding to revising and editing questions:

- Read the passage carefully. Note that all the sentences in the passage may be numbered.

- Multiple-choice questions that follow the passage may refer to a specific numbered sentence in the passage. Reread the sentence referred to in the question. Before you evaluate the choices, determine what error, if any, has been made in the sentence. Then read the choices and choose the correct answer.

Getting a Head Start on Writing in Response to a Prompt

A writing prompt on a test may consist of a writing topic and a suggestion on how you can write about it. The writing prompt on the test may relate to a literary passage or it may be a stand-alone task such as a persuasive essay on a given topic. Here are some tips for writing a response to a prompt:

- Read the prompt carefully. Think about what it asks you to do. If you misread a prompt or fail to interpret a prompt properly, your written response will be incorrect.

- Remember that the prompt may be linked to a reading passage. Think about the connection. If appropriate, use details from the passage in your response, but you are not required to do this.

- Read any reminder statements and take them seriously. They are meant to be a checklist. Read them before you write your response and after you write your response to make sure you have addressed them.

- Use a planning page to brainstorm ideas and organize them.

- Select an approach and an audience for your response. Remember that your audience can be anyone but yourself.

- Remember that you must show not only that you can write a correct answer but also that you can write a thoughtful and insightful one. In other words, show how well you have thought about the topic of the prompt. This is an opportunity for your higher-order thinking skills to shine.

- Let your own individual style show through. Develop a voice that sounds authentic and original and maintain this voice throughout your response.

- Revise and proofread your response. It will be evaluated based on how effectively it is written and how well it adheres to the conventions of standard written English. Check the organization. Consider whether or not it is focused.

Measuring Up with Building Stamina

Unique features of this book are the **Building Stamina** review sections, which are designed to give you practice and build your confidence for completing higher-level thinking activities. These activities will include answering questions that cover multiple California Content Standards. Each chapter in Measuring Up ends with a **Building Stamina** section. The challenging questions in this section will build your stamina and understanding to succeed with difficult activities.

- **Building Stamina** in Part 1

  The **Building Stamina** sections in Part 1 are designed to give you practice with challenging reading passages and questions. They provide the same kind of selections you will be expected to read. They also have the kinds of questions you will be expected to answer to show how well you have mastered the California Content Standards. Following Chapters 1 through 3, each **Building Stamina** section includes one reading selection with ten multiple-choice questions

- **Building Stamina** in Part 2

  The **Building Stamina** sections in Part 2 provide revising, editing, and writing practice.

By the time you come to the end of this Measuring Up book, you will have reviewed and practiced the California Content Standards and built up your stamina to answer tough questions. In other words, you will have all that you need to be a success. Now it's up to you!

Chapter 1 Word Analysis and Vocabulary Development

In this chapter, you will learn:

- how to use spelling patterns when reading;
- how to break words into syllables;
- how to decode words with more than one syllable;
- how to understand abbreviations;
- how to use correct plurals;
- how to read fluently;
- how to understand synonyms and antonyms;
- how to use prefixes and suffixes;
- how to understand multiple-meaning words.

Chapter 2 Reading Comprehension

In this chapter, you will learn:

- how to use the parts of a book to find information;
- how to state your purpose for reading;
- how to identify the author's purpose;
- how to ask questions;
- how to restate facts and details;
- how to identify cause and effect;
- how to read charts, graphs, and diagrams;
- how to follow instructions.

Chapter 3 Literary Response and Analysis

In this chapter, you will learn:

- how to understand plot;
- how to understand characters;
- how to understand setting;
- how to compare stories;
- how to understand sound devices in poetry.

Lesson 1   Understand Spelling Patterns

Focus on California Content Standards

Standard 2RW1.1 Recognize and use knowledge of spelling patterns (e.g., diphthongs, special vowel spellings) when reading.

When you read, you often find new words that you may not know. Here are three simple things you can do to figure out these new words:

• Look at how the word is spelled.

• Link the letters to the sounds they spell.

• Say the word aloud.

In many words, two or more letters work together to spell one **vowel** sound. Here are some letter groups and the sounds they spell.

Letters	Sounds	Words
ai, ay	long /a/	b**ai**t, d**ay**
ee, aa	long /e/ or short /e/	h**ea**t, s**ee**m h**ea**d, d**ea**th
oa, ow	long /o/	s**oa**k, gl**ow**
ou, ough	short /u/	c**ou**ntry, r**ou**gh

Sometimes two vowels can work together to create a special sound.

Letters	Sounds	Words
oi, oy	/oi/	**oi**l, t**oy**
ou, ow	/ou/	l**ou**d, t**ow**n

**Guided
Reading
Instruction**

Directions Read the following poem. Use the questions on the side of the page to guide you. Then answer the questions.

The Country Mouse
by Djeema Jensen

1 Once there was a curious boy
Who was absolutely filled with joy.

2 One day not far from his orange house
He met a little country mouse.
The country mouse was eating hay
But the curious boy wanted him to play.

The boy was very quick to say:
3 "Oh, please little
mouse
don't be a louse.
Let's have some fun
There's no need to run.
4 Look! It's going to rain
Let's hide in the train
And look for treasure
In this cloudy weather."

To which the mouse replied:
"Oh, my, my dear boy
That train is such a tiny toy!
Perhaps you'd rather sail
Across that giant yellow pail!
And maybe we'll find a silly snail
Who'll tell us a fantastic tale."

Well, the boy and the mouse
Now live in the house
And every day they go out to play
5 In the giant pail with the tiny snail
Who is very good at spinning a tale!

Guided Questions

1 Read the first line. Circle the word that has the same vowel sound as the word <u>point</u>. Say the word aloud.

2 Find the word <u>house</u>, and circle it. What word in the next line has the same vowel sound? What word contains the letter <u>ou</u> but has a different vowel sound?

3 Circle the word that has the same long /e/ sound as in <u>cheese</u>. What letters spell this sound?

4 Circle the letters <u>ai</u> in <u>rain</u>. Write two words that have the same long /a/ sound.

5 Circle the words in this line that have a long /a/ sound. Then choose one of the words. Write a sentence of your own that tells about a <u>snail</u>.

1. Read the lines below.

> "Oh, my, my dear boy
> That train is such a tiny toy!

Circle the words in the box that have the same vowel sound as <u>boy</u> and <u>toy</u>.

coin	moon	cloud	oil	noise

2. Read the line below. Circle the letters that spell the vowel sound in <u>snail</u>.

> And maybe we'll find a silly snail.

3. Say each word aloud in the box below.

tray	chain	clown	bounce	day
soil	toy	seem	heat	greet

Sort the words in the box above. Make sure it has the same vowel sound as the word at the top of each column. Then write the word in the correct column.

stay	point	pound	team

Apply

Directions Read the story below. Then answer the questions that follow.

Lulu and Jackson
by Emmy Clark

It was late afternoon. Lulu lay still in her burrow under a stone. It was very pleasant. The ground was cool. The air smelled like honey. It must be the sweet peas, she thought. Lulu liked flowers. She also smelled raspberries. She really liked raspberry seeds. It was time to peek outside. Jackson should have been here by now. Jackson was her best friend.

She looked over at the flower garden. She was surprised that he was not in his usual spot. His favorite place to sit was on the lilac bush. He had a special green leaf that he liked. It was the best place to smell the teeny purple flowers. Sometimes he even liked to count them. One time he got up to 236. On warm summer nights, he often liked to sleep there.

"Where could he be?" Lulu asked herself. "I wonder if something is wrong?" She worried about Jackson all the time.

Just then, she heard a little chirp. Lulu crawled out from under the rock and looked around.

"Lulu, it's me, Jackson," said Jackson in a very little voice.

"Where are you, Jackson?" chirped Lulu. She was very upset now. Jackson usually had a strong chirp. Now it was very weak. She wondered what was wrong.

"Lulu, I'm over here," said Jackson. "Look! I'm under the lilac bush."

Lulu looked. Then she took one giant leap towards him. Not bad, she thought to herself. I just jumped about three feet!

"Okay, Jackson, what is going on?" chirped Lulu. "I've been quite worried about you."

"I'm worried about me, too," chirped Jackson in a very little voice now. "Last night the Cricket Chorus had practice. I was chirping away, and I fell off the stage. It was a long way down. I caught my wing on a blade of tough grass. Now I can hardly chirp. I don't know what to do. Tonight is the spring Cricket Chorus Concert," he chirped in a tiny, tiny voice.

"Oh, no!" chirped Lulu. "You have a big solo, right?"

"That's right," chirped Jackson. He could hardly make a sound.

"Well, let me look at your wing," chirped Lulu softly. "Maybe it just needs a little fixing."

Lulu looked at Jackson's wing. She saw a small bruise. It was about the size of a grain of sand.

"Ouch!" chirped Jackson. "That hurts! Don't touch it."

"Jackson, crawl out from under the bush," chirped Lulu. "You need sun. We can sit on our favorite rock. The sun will heal your wing quickly."

"All right," Jackson made a squeaky little noise.

"Jackson, please don't use your voice. Be very quiet, okay?" chirped Lulu. "Let's just sit here in the sun, and watch the butterflies."

Jackson nodded at Lulu. About two hours later, Lulu asked Jackson to try a chirp. Jackson gave one slow chirp. He sounded better.

"That's pretty good, Jackson," chirped Lulu. "By tonight, I think you'll have your big sound back. Your voice will be loud enough."

"Thanks, Lulu, you really are my best friend," chirped Jackson carefully.

1. Read this sentence from the story.

> It must be the sweet peas, she thought.

What two words have the same long /e/ sound as in <u>sheep</u>?
Circle those words. What letters spell this vowel sound?

_____

- -

_____

2. What words below have the same vowel sound as the word <u>ground</u>?
Circle them.

> flower   could   ouch   look

3. Read the sentence below.

> "All right," Jackson made a squeaky little noise.
> "Jackson, don't use your voice. Be very quiet, okay?" chirped Lulu.

Circle the two words that have the same vowel sound as the
word <u>joy.</u>

Assessment Practice   **Directions** Answer the questions based on the story you just read.

1 **Which word below does NOT have the same vowel sound as <u>grain</u>?**

A rain
B paint
C said
D may

2 **Which word has the same vowel sound as <u>tough</u>?**

A scout
B plow
C count
D touch

Focus on California Content Standards

Lesson 2   Break Words into Syllables

Standard 2RW1.2 Apply knowledge of basic syllabication rules when reading (e.g., vowel-consonant-vowel = su/per; vowel-consonant/consonant vowel – sup/per).

When you read, you will see long words. Sometimes you won't know how to say them. Here is what you can do to learn how to say the word.

- Break the word into smaller parts. These smaller parts are called **syllables.** A syllable has only one vowel sound. When you break a word into syllables, it is easier to read the parts.

- Sound out each syllable. Then put the parts back together. Say the word aloud a few times. It will help you remember how to say the word.

Here are two rules to help you break words into syllables.

- When a word has two **consonants,** between two vowels, break the word between the consonants. The letter y sometimes works like a vowel. Look at these words.

    hap-py   fin-ger   mag-net

- When a word has a **vowel-consonant-vowel** pattern, break the word after the first vowel.

    me-tal   po-lite   se-cret

A **dictionary** can also help you. It shows how a word is broken. For example:

    sil-ly   ho-tel   ga-rage

Guided Reading Instruction

Directions Read the story below. Use the questions on the side of the page to guide you. You may use a dictionary.

1 The Thanksgiving Dinner That Almost Wasn't
by Marilyn Kratz

"Would you like to come to my house for Thanksgiving dinner?" Woodchuck asked Rabbit, Raccoon, and Skunk.

"Yes, thank you," said Rabbit.

2 "I'd enjoy that," said Raccoon.

"Count me in," said Skunk. "Let's all bring something. Then Woodchuck won't have so much to do."

"Good idea," said Raccoon.

"Yes, let us help," agreed Rabbit.

"Why, thank you," said Woodchuck. "I'll see you on Thanksgiving Day."

Early on Thanksgiving Day, Woodchuck tidied up his burrow. 3 He made an acorn pie. Then he waited anxiously to see what delicious foods his friends would bring.

Guided Questions

1 Say the word <u>almost</u> aloud. How many syllables does this word have? Break this word into syllables. What rule did you follow?

2 Circle the word <u>enjoy</u>. Say it aloud. Break this word into syllables.

3 Say the word <u>acorn</u>. How many syllables does this word have? Break this word into syllables. What rule did you follow?

Rabbit came first.

"I made a pumpkin place card for each of us," said Rabbit.

"Oh!" said Woodchuck, trying to hide his surprise. "What a good idea."

Next came Raccoon. "I brought these beautiful autumn leaves to decorate the table," he said.

"Oh . . . how nice," said Woodchuck.

Then Skunk arrived. "I brought a book of stories to read after we eat," she said.

"Thank you, Skunk," said Woodchuck. Now he felt worried.

4 "I don't smell our dinner," said Rabbit.

"Are we too early?" asked Raccoon.

"I could read a story out loud while we wait for dinner to finish cooking," suggested Skunk.

Woodchuck plopped down in his chair. "I'm sorry," he said. "When you said something, I thought you meant the food. I only made dessert."

5 Rabbit and Raccoon and Skunk looked at each other, and everyone began to laugh.

"We all misunderstood," said Skunk.

"I have an idea," said Woodchuck. "Let's have our Thanksgiving dinner tomorrow. My burrow is tidied up, so I'll have plenty of time to cook."

"Good idea," said Rabbit.

"I agree," said Skunk.

Guided Questions

4 Read this sentence. Circle the two words that follow this rule: When a word has two consonants, break the word between the two consonants. Say the words aloud.

5 Say the word <u>began</u>. Circle each syllable. Think of another word that follows the rule for breaking this word.

"And this time we'll all bring some food to help with the feast," said Raccoon.

"Yes, said Rabbit. "We'll have a wonderful Day-After-Thanksgiving feast. After all, any day is a good day to be thankful."

1. Read the sentence from the story below.

> Early on Thanksgiving Day, Woodchuck tidied up his burrow.

Which word in this sentence means "a place where an animal lives"? Circle it. Then break the word into syllables. What rule did you follow?

_____

_____

_____

_____

_____

_____

2. Break the word <u>carrot</u> into syllables. Circle the words in the box that follow the same rule.

happen	insect	water	whiskers	faster

Apply   **Directions**   Read the story below. Then answer the questions that follow.

Marmalade
by Lucy Clark Owens

Tamara really wanted a bunny. That's what she thought about all the time. She'd already asked her mom about twenty times. Today she thought that she'd try one more time. She found her mom outside. She was in their small garden. She was staring at a plant leaf.

"Hi, Mom," said Tamara.

"Hi," replied her mom. "What's up?"

"What are you staring at, Mom?" asked Tamara. She looked at the leaf.

" A ladybug," she answered. "We have a little bug family here."

"That's cool," Tamara said looking at the ladybugs.

"Very cool," said her mom.

"Mom, I really, really want a bunny," said Tamara. "It's the only pet I've ever wanted.'

"Bunnies need a lot of care," said her mom.

"Mom, please," Tamara begged.

"Tamara, it's just not possible," her mother said gently. "Think of another pet. What about a kitten? I'll take you to the animal shelter. You can adopt a kitten. A kitten would be perfect. Or, what about an ant farm? You like to watch the ants when we go to the beach."

This last comment made Tamara groan. Her mom always had weird pet ideas.

Her mother went on, "I saw where we can buy an ant farm. It was in a catalog. Do you want me to order one for you?"

Sometimes it drove Tamara nuts when her mom said stuff like this. Her mom was a science teacher. That can be a big problem! Her mom liked ants. She liked all insects. She'd been studying them for years.

"No, Mom, I don't want an ant farm," said Tamara giggling. "I can't cuddle an ant. I want a bunny to cuddle."

"Okay, I can understand that!" said her mom. "Well then, what's wrong with a kitten? You can cuddle a kitten."

"C'mon, let's just go take a look," said her mother. "You don't have anything to lose!"

"Oh, okay!" said Tamara.

Mrs. Tuttle drove Tamara to the animal shelter. She was glad Mr. Donovan was there. Tamara knew him pretty well. She dropped by a lot to see if he had bunnies, but he never did.

"Well, what can I do for you today?" asked Mr. Donovan.

"I want to see a kitten," Tamara said. "Do you happen to have any?"

"Sure enough. Mrs. Martin brought in four kittens this morning. Let's go take a look!" he said.

Mr. Donovan took them over to a big playpen. Four kittens were playing. They were the cutest orange kittens Tamara had ever seen.

All of a sudden, Tamara changed her mind. She just had to have one of these little balls of fur.

"Mom," she squealed. "They are SO cute! Can I pick one?"

"Of course, you can," her mom said. "How are you going to choose? I can't even tell them apart."

Neither could Tamara. She just kept looking. She began to notice one kitten. It was the most playful. It would nip the others. Then it would run and hide in the shredded paper. Then it would look at Tamara.

"Mr. Donovan, may I hold that kitten?" Tamara asked.

"Of course," said Mr. Donovan. He picked up the little kitten gently. Then he handed it to Tamara. "You picked a cute one! Look at her sweet face."

Tamara cuddled the kitten close to her. The kitten felt just right in her arms. This was the kitten for her. She held her up. She looked at her face.

"Hi, Marmalade," she said. Then she smiled a big smile.

"Marmalade!" said Mr. Donovan. "That's a good name."

"She is the same color as orange marmalade," said Tamara. "That's my favorite jam."

A few days later, Tamara wrote Mr. Donovan a letter. She told him that Marmalade was the perfect pet. She did not say one word about bunnies!

 Measuring Up® to the California Content Standards

1. Read this sentence.

> You can adopt a kitten.

Circle the word <u>adopt</u>. Say it aloud. Break this word into syllables. If you could adopt a pet, what pet would you adopt?

_____

- -

_____

2. Read this sentence.

> This last comment made Tamara groan. Her mom always had weird pet ideas.

Which two words follow this rule: When a word has two consonants between two vowels, break the word between the consonants? Circle the words. Break each word into syllables.

_____

- -

_____

Assessment Practice   **Directions** Answer the questions based on the story you just read.

1 **Which word has been broken into syllables correctly?**

A s-udden

B sudd-en

C sudde-n

D sud-den

2 **Read the sentence below.**

> Marmalade was the <u>perfect</u> pet.

Which of the following shows the correct way to break <u>perfect</u>?

A per-fect

B perf-ect

C perfe-ct

D perfec-t

Focus on California Content Standards

Lesson 3   **Decode Words With More Than One Syllable**

Standard 2RW1.3   Decode two-syllable nonsense words and regular multisyllable words.

Many words you read are long. They may have two or three syllables. Sometimes words have even more syllables. You can sound out long words. This will help you learn how to read them.

Look at these words. Notice where the words are broken into syllables. Say them aloud.

coun-try   croc-o-dile   hel-i-cop-ter

Sometimes writers will make up words. These words may have base words that are real, and real meanings, but they are not actually words. When a word looks new to you, sound out the word. Then say it aloud. It may sound like a word you know. It may also help you figure out the meaning.

Guided Reading Instruction

Directions Read the following poem. Use the questions on the side of the page to guide you. Then answer the questions.

1 Mr. Bidery's Spidery Garden
by David M. McCord

Poor old Mr. Bidery.
2 His garden's awfully spiderery:
Bugs use it as a hidery.

In April it was seedery,
By May a mass of weedery:
3 And oh, the bugs! How greedery.

White flowers out or buddery,
4 Potatoes made it spuddery:
And when it rained, what muddery!

June days grow long and shaddery;
Bullfrog forgets his taddery;
The spider legs his laddery.

With cabbages so odory,
Snapdragon soon explodery,
At twilight all is toadery.

Young corn still far from foddery
No sign of goldenrodery,
Yet feeling low and doddery

Is poor old Mr. Bidery,
5 His garden lush and spidery,
His apples green, not cidery.

Pea-picking *is* so poddery!

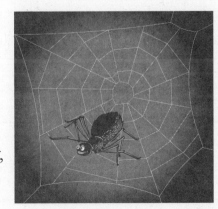

Guided Questions

1 Say the title aloud. How many syllables does <u>Spidery</u> have? Break this word into syllables. What other word in the title has the same number of syllables?

2 Circle the word <u>awfully</u>. Say it aloud. Break it into syllables.

3 Circle the word <u>greedery</u>. Say it aloud. Break it into syllables. The word greedery is a nonsense word. What real word do you see in it? How were the bugs greedy?

4 Circle the word <u>potatoes</u>. Say it aloud. Break it into syllables.

5 Circle the word <u>garden</u>. Say it aloud. Break it into syllables. What is one reason Mr. Bidery's garden is such a mess?

1. Read the line below.

> And when it rained, what muddery!

Which word has three syllables? Circle the word. This is a nonsense word. What smaller word do you see in it? Write your own sentence using the smaller word about what happened to the garden when it rained.

_____

- -

_____

_____

- -

_____

- -

_____

2. Read the line below.

> At twilight all is toadery.

Underline the word <u>twilight</u>. Say it aloud. Break it into syllables. What happens at twilight? At what time of day is twilight?

_____

- -

_____

_____

- -

_____

_____

- -

_____

 Measuring Up® to the California Content Standards

Apply   **Directions** Read the poem below. Then answer the questions that follow.

The Frizzy Froopster
by Molly Lowry

I met a silly creature with hair that was bruzzy
And a long striped tail that was ever so fuzzy.
On his feet were blue galoshes
On his hands were pink faloshes.
On his head he wore a fedley
It was such silly medley!
Around his neck he wore a pinkish bundee
And on his wrist he wore an ice cream sundae!
I asked him for a bittle scoop
But he gave me just a fittle froop.
Well, silly, nilly, frizzy froopster.
I'll get my own vanilla scoopster!

1. Circle the nonsense words below that have the same number of syllables as <u>bruzzy</u>.

| fruzzy | gluz | fripsey | grop | blozzy |

2. Read this line.

On his feet were blue galoshes

Circle <u>galoshes</u>. Say it aloud. Break it into syllables. What are galoshes?

_____

- -
_____

_____
- -
_____

_____
- -
_____

3. Read this line.

And on his wrist he wore a sundae!

Circle the word <u>sundae</u>. Say it aloud. Break this word into syllables. Write the name of an ice cream treat that has more than one syllable. Break it into syllables.

_____
- -
_____

_____
- -
_____

 Measuring Up® to the California Content Standards

Assessment Practice   **Directions** Answer the questions based on the poem you just read.

1 **Read the line below.**

On his hands were pink <u>faloshes</u>.

Which of the following shows the correct way to break the nonsense word <u>faloshes</u>?

A fa-loshes

B fal-oshes

C fa-losh-es

D falosh-es

2 **Which word has been broken into syllables correctly?**

A med-ley

B medle-y

C medl-ey

D me-d-ley

Focus on California Content Standards

Lesson 4   Understand Abbreviations

Standard 2RW.1.4 Recognize common abbreviations (e.g. Jan., Sun., Mr., St.)

There are many words that you can abbreviate (pronounced a-bree-vee-ate). When you **abbreviate,** you make a word shorter. When you write an **abbreviation,** you start with a capital letter and end with a period (.).

When you say an abbreviated word, remember to say the full word. For example, when you see Mon., you say Monday.

Here are some words that you can abbreviate.

- Days of the week

  Monday **Mon.**   Wednesday **Wed.**   Saturday **Sat.**

- Months of the year

  January **Jan.**   August **Aug.**   October **Oct.**

- Titles of people that are used with names

  Mr. James Woods   **Mrs.** Evelyn Bridges

When you pronounce Mr., you say Mister. When you pronounce Mrs., you say Missus.

- Addresses of people and places

  Avenue **Ave.**   Drive **Dr.**   Street **St.**   Road **Rd.**

Guided Reading Instruction

Directions Read the letter below. Use the questions on the side to guide your reading.

1 August 1, 2005

Dear Lindy,

Hi! I'm visiting my Aunt Tallulah. I arrived on Monday. We are having a lot of fun. She lives near the ocean. Every day we go to the beach. We walk along the shore and collect shells. My shell collection is getting bigger every day. Sometimes we see baby elephant seals. **2** They were born on January 1, 2005. Now, they are very big! I like to draw pictures of them. Look at this picture! They have such cute faces.

Some afternoons we go into town for ice cream cones. We also go to a farmer's market. It's always on a Saturday, and we buy corn-on-the cob. It's my favorite vegetable.

I hope that you are having a good time at camp. Did you learn how to dive off the diving board yet? Maybe you can write me a card. The address at my aunt's house is:

Miss Betsy Sims
3 In care of Missus Tallulah Lopez
125 Butterfly Rd.
Pismo Beach, California 93449

Guided Questions

1 Read the date. How should you abbreviate August?

2 Circle the abbreviation for a month of the year. What is the full word?

3 How do you abbreviate Missus?

4 I will be home on Wednesday, August 31. Can we get together on Saturday, Sept. 2? Let's go for a bike ride in the park. Call me as soon as you get home, okay?

Your friend,
Betsy

Guided Questions

4 How would you abbreviate August 31? What happens on that date?

5 On what date does Betsy want to ride bikes with Lindy? Write the word for the month.

1. In which month are baby sea elephants born? How would you abbreviate this month?

_____

- -

_____

2. What is the street address where Aunt Tallulah lives? Rewrite the street address. Do not use an abbreviation.

_____

- -

_____

3. Look at these words and abbreviations. Rewrite them to show the word or abbreviation.

Mister	
	Nov.
	Ave.
Street	

Copying is illegal. Measuring Up® to the California Content Standards

Apply   **Directions** Read the newspaper below. Then answer the questions that follow.

The Big Buzz!

Friday, March 11, 2005
Spring Fever!
by Mrs. Colby's
Second Grade Class

It's almost spring. It will be here on March 20. We can't wait. It will be time to plant flowers. This year we want to plant flowers that butterflies like. We learned in science class that they like marigolds. If you want to help plant flowers in the school garden, see Krista! She needs at least 20 kids. We hope to plant the flowers on Thursday, April 8.

Bird Watch
by Dylan Bishop

Do you like birds? Do you want to learn more about them? Come to our bird meeting. It's on Mon., Mar. 14. Miss Kate Ford will be there. She works at Bird House Place. She knows birds very well. She will take kids on a bird walk on a Saturday, April 9. If you want to go, sign the paper. It's on the bulletin board. Remember, it's time for robins and bluebirds.

Flower Fun!
by Cordelia Bishop

Would you like to make some cool flowers? Next Tuesday, Mrs. Pottle is going to show students how to make button flowers. If you want to buy some buttons before the class, go to The Button Shop at 124 Main Street. Ask for Rosie. She's the button queen. She'll show you the most fun buttons. She is there on Mon., Tues., and Thurs. You can find her at their other shop at 78 Maple Dr. on Wed. and Fri.. Don't forget the date now!

Tadpole Tales
by Mr. Swift's Second Grade Class

It's tadpole time. Saturday, April 23 is the BIG day. We're off to Duck Pond. Mister Tucker says that we'll see a lot of tadpoles this year. We might even see that huge toad we saw last year! Callie is bringing her dad's tape recorder. We want to record frog sounds and buzzing for our science class. We're going to meet at 10 o'clock at Freddy's house. He lives at 56 Pine Avenue.

---

1. On what day is Mrs. Colby's class going to plant flowers? How would you abbreviate this date?

_____

- -

_____

- -

_____

2. On what day is the bird meeting? Rewrite the sentence without using any abbreviations.

_____

- -

_____

3. Who wrote "Tadpole Tales?" How do you spell out Mr.?

_____

- -

_____

Assessment Practice   **Directions** Answer the questions based on the story you just read.

1 **Read this sentence.**

| It will be here on March 20. |

What is the correct abbreviation for March?

A   mar

B   Mar

C   Mar.

D   Ma.

2 **Read this sentence.**

| She will take kids on a bird walk on a Saturday, April 9. |

What is the correct abbreviation for Saturday, April 9?

A   Sat Apr 9

B   Sat., April 9

C   Satur., April 9

D   Sat., Apr. 9

     Measuring Up® to the California Content Standards

Focus on California Content Standards

Lesson 5 **Use Correct Plurals**

Standard 2RW1.5 Identify and correctly use regular plurals (e.g., -s, -es, -ies) and irregular plurals (e.g., *fly/flies, wife/wives*).

Plural means "more than one." A noun can be **singular** (one) or plural (more than one). Here are some rules you can follow to make the plural of a noun.

- Add -**s** to form the plural of most nouns.

beetle	crayon	duck	shovel
beetle**s**	crayon**s**	duck**s**	shovel**s**

- Add -**es** to form the plural of nouns that end in <u>s</u> or <u>ss</u>, <u>x</u>, <u>ch</u>, or <u>sh</u>.

addre**ss**	fo**x**	pea**ch**	dis**h**
address**es**	fox**es**	peach**es**	dish**es**

- Add -**ies** to form the plural of nouns that end in a consonant plus <u>y</u>. Remember to change the <u>y</u> to -<u>i</u> and add <u>es</u>.

countr**y**	bunn**y**	stor**y**	librar**y**
countr**ies**	bunn**ies**	stor**ies**	librar**ies**

- Add <u>s</u> to form the plural of nouns that end in a vowel plus <u>y</u>.

bo**y**	donke**y**	holida**y**	pla**y**
boy**s**	donkey**s**	holiday**s**	play**s**

- Some words have **irregular** nouns. They do not follow the rules above.

goose	mouse	child	tooth
geese	mice	children	teeth

Guided Reading Instruction

Directions   Read the story below. Use the questions on the side to guide your reading.

1 The Moonbeam Party
by Dorothea Gilbert

It was almost dark. Bluebell sat near the peach tree. Where was Purdy, she wondered. Why wasn't he in the garden? It was their favorite time to eat. 2 She looked over at the radishes. Purdy wasn't there. That's very strange, Bluebell thought. Purdy never misses a chance for a fresh radish.

Bluebell ate one more berry. Bluebell liked berries. Sometimes she ate too many. It made her whiskers turn blue. She didn't care. She loved them anyway.

Bluebell and Purdy never argued over food. Maybe that is why they were best friends. Well, no, that wasn't the reason. The reason was because they both loving chasing moonbeams.

3 Bluebell heard a peach drop off the tree. She looked behind her. Purdy had pulled the branch down and was shaking it.

"Purdy, what you are doing?" asked Bluebell.

"I'm getting a few peaches," said Purdy.

"What's wrong, Purdy? You seem very upset," said Bluebell.

"I am V-E-R-Y upset," said Purdy. "I guess that you haven't heard. I have very bad N-E-W-S." When Purdy was upset, he spelled out certain words.

Guided Questions

1 Circle the word <u>party</u>. What is the plural? What rule did you follow?

2 Circle the word <u>radishes</u>. Why did the writer add <u>-es</u>?

3 Circle the word <u>peach</u>. What is the plural? What rule did you follow?

"What news?" asked Bluebell. Bluebell stopped eating. She hopped over to Purdy.

4 "W-E-L-L, I saw Deer in the meadow. He was eating a lot of flowers. He told me B-A-D news. There is going to be a big storm tonight," Purdy said sadly.

4 Circle the word meadow. What is the plural? What was Deer eating?

"Rain?" yelled Bluebell. "It can't rain tonight."

"I know, I know," said Purdy. "It's the night of our moonbeam party."

"Oh, no!" Everyone is so excited," said Bluebell. "What shall we do?"

"I don't know," said Purdy. "I guess we can have it another night."

"But, Purdy, it's full moon tonight! It's the best night for chasing moonbeams. You know that! The moonbeams are so bright when there is a full moon."

"I know! I know!" said Purdy.

Just then, a drop of rain plopped right down on the ground. Then another drop fell.

"Quick!" said Purdy. "Let's go hide under the berry bush."

"Okay," said Bluebell.

They hopped very fast over to the nearest berry bush. They just sat there. They could not stop staring at the raindrops.

"Oh, well," sighed Bluebell. "We can plan another moonbeam party for August."

"You're right," said Purdy. "We could also have a shooting star party. August is the perfect month for shooting stars."

1. Read this sentence.

> Why wasn't he in the garden?

Write the plural for garden. Who wasn't in the garden? Use the word garden in your answer.

_____

- -

_____

2. Read this sentence.

> "Quick!" said Purdy. "Let's go hide under the berry bush."

Write the plural for bush. What rule did you follow?

_____

- -

_____

3. Look at these words. Write the plural.

banana	
fox	
butterfly	
child	

Copying is illegal.

Apply   **Directions** Read the story below. Then answer the questions that follow.

Night Sounds
by Lucy Clark Owens

Gabriel and Pedro sat on a log near the campfire. They were waiting. Any minute now the night sounds would begin. They loved sitting here in the woods. So far, the only night sound was buzz, buzz, buzz. Little insects were flying all around them. Pedro swatted one on his arm and squashed it.

"What's this insect?" asked Gabriel pointing to it.

"It's called a pesky fly!" answered Pedro. Then he chuckled. "Good name for an insect, huh?"

"Sure is," laughed Gabriel.

"Let's put another log on the fire," said Gabriel. "Insects don't like smoke."

Pedro walked over to the pile of firewood and got a log. He put it on the fire. Then Gabriel poked the fire a few times. More smoke started to rise.

"Well, that's better," said Gabriel. "Hey, I wonder where Dad is? It's time for our snack. I wish he'd bring some of those brownies we had for lunch."

"Maybe he's over in the barn," said Pedro. "He said that a fox almost got into the chicken coop last night."

"Really?" said Gabriel. "That hasn't happened in a while. Those poor chicks. They must have been running all over the place."

"Are you sure we're in the right place?" asked Pedro. "We haven't heard one owl sound, yet."

"Yeah, I'm sure. This is where we were last night. We heard some great sounds," Gabby replied. "We just have to be patient. Don't forget we found that owl feather yesterday. It was right over there under that fir tree. I think that tree is where it roosts. Maybe there's a whole family up there."

"Where did you put that feather, anyway?" asked Pedro.

"It's in my magic pouch that Mom made for me," said Gabriel.

"Listen, Gabriel. Did you hear that sound? It's right over there. Wow! That's him."

Gabriel and Pedro stopped talking and listened. *Whoop-wu-hu-hoo. Whoop-wu-hu-hoo.* Then it was quiet. Then there was another sound. *Hoo-hoo-hoo.* Pedro grabbed Gabriel's arm.

Then he whispered, "Do you hear that? Do you think there are two different owls here?"

"I think so. We know the *whoop-wu-hu-hoo* sound. It's a male spotted owl," Gabriel said quietly. "But what's the *hoo-hoo-hoo?* Do you know?"

"I think it's a screech owl," whispered Pedro.

"Amazing! We've never heard one before," said Gabriel.

"I know," said Pedro.

Both of the boys sat quietly and listened. Over and over again, they heard the same two owl sounds. Then the sounds stopped.

Suddenly, something swooped down in front of them.

"WOW!" said Pedro and Gabriel at the same time. They both jumped and pointed toward the night sky.

"Amazing! Did you see its claws? Did you see its spots?" said Pedro. "It's the spotted owl. Maybe it's looking for a moth. Maybe it has a baby owl to feed."

"C'mon, let's put out the fire and go tell Dad," said Gabriel. "It's our best owl story this summer."

"No, let's wait," said Pedro. "I want to hear more night sounds."

"Okay," said Gabriel.

For another hour, the boys sat on that log and listened. They both agreed it was a very good night for owl toots and hoots.

1. Read this sentence.

"It's called a pesky fly!" answered Pedro.

Circle the word <u>fly</u>. Write the plural. What rule did you follow?

_____

- -

_____

- -

_____

- -

_____

2. Imagine that a family member made brownies. He or she gives you only one to eat. Do you spell the singular word browny or brownie? Look it up in a dictionary to see if you're right.

_____

- -

_____

3. Circle all the words that use the same rule to form a plural as the word <u>baby</u>. Then write the plural of each one.

county   moth   city   sky   log

_____

- -

_____

- -

_____

Assessment Practice

Directions Answer the questions based on the story you just read.

1 **What is the correct way to write the word that means more than one mouse?**

A mices

B mouses

C mice

D micies

2 **Read this sentence.**

"It's in my magic pouch that Mom made for me," said Gabriel.

What is the correct way to write the word that means more than one pouch?

A pouchies

B pouchs

C pouchss

D pouches

Focus on California Content Standards

| Lesson 6 | Read Fluently |

Standard 2RW1.6 Read aloud fluently and accurately and with appropriate intonation and expression.

It is important to know how to read aloud. This helps you understand what you are reading.

Here are five things you can do to help when you read aloud:

- **Think about each word.** Make sure you know what every word means. If you see a word you don't know, sound it out. Say each syllable aloud. Then put the word back together. Say it aloud again. If you still don't know what the word means, look it up in a dictionary.

- **Read smoothly.** If you stumble over a word, repeat it a few times. If you can't understand the word, look it up in a dictionary. Find out how to pronounce it. Say it aloud slowly a few times. Keep saying the word until it is easy for you to say.

- **Read easily.** You may have trouble with some long or difficult words. Say each one slowly. Reread them until you can say every word easily.

- **Understand What the Characters Say.** Think about what you are reading. Should the words be read in a goofy voice? Should the words be read in a sad voice? Should the words be read in different voices? Using different voices will make the story more fun for others to hear.

- **Read with Expression.** When you read aloud, remember to read with expression. Read in a voice that shows feeling. It can be a happy feeling. It can be a silly feeling. It might be an angry feeling. Read this sentence:

> "I won! I won the race!" yelled Amy, jumping up and down.

Think about how Amy said, "I won! I won the race!" Most likely, she yelled these words very loudly and very happily. She was so excited.

Directions Read the poem below. Use the questions on the side to guide your reading. Then answer the questions that follow.

Ship Shape
by Jennifer Kramer

Guided Questions

1 Swab the decks with mop and pail.
Pull the ropes and raise the sail.

2 Polish rails from fore to aft.
Raise the anchor, patch the raft.

Check the ship from bow to stern.
Give the captain's wheel a turn.

Blast the horn, one last TOOT! TOOT!
3 Then, hand to brow, a ship salute.

We're setting sail. **4** We've done it, crew.
5 Our ship's in shape, and we are, too!

1 Circle the word swab. The a makes the same sound you hear in father. Say swab aloud. *Swab* means "clean." This word is used a lot by sailors. What did the sailors swab? Why?

2 Say this line a few times. Then circle the words fore and aft. What do you think these words mean?

3 Circle the word salute. Break it into syllables. What does salute mean?

4 Circle the word crew. It rhymes with do. Say crew aloud. What does crew mean?

5 Pretend you are setting sail on a boat. How would you read the last line?

1. Read the line below.

> Polish rails from fore to aft.

What does polish mean? You may use your dictionary to help you.
What does the crew polish on the boat?

_____

- -

_____

- -

_____

2. Read the line below.

> Raise the anchor, patch the raft.

What is a raft? You may use a dictionary to help you. When you
patch a raft, what do you do? Use patch in your answer.

_____

- -

_____

- -

_____

3. Read the line below.

> Check the ship from bow to stern.

Circle the words in this line that mean "front" and "back." You may
use your dictionary to help you.

_____

- -

_____

Apply   **Directions** Read the poem below. Then answer the questions
that follow.

Broccoli Dog
by Lynne Berry

My puppy likes broccoli.
It's terribly odd.
She doesn't like carrots
Or cabbage
Or cod.
She doesn't like pizza or waffles or steak.
She doesn't like cookies or caramel cake.
She doesn't like bacon or bisquits or ham
Or custard or mustard or strawberry jam.
She doesn't like doughnuts or crackers or peas.
She doesn't like apples or smelly blue cheese.
She doesn't like noodles or olives or roast
Or coffee or toffee or cinnamon toast.
She eats only broccoli—
Bushel and bunch!
Broccoli at breakfast,
At dinner,
And lunch.

               Measuring Up® to the California Content Standards

1. Read the title of the poem. How would you break the word <u>broccoli</u> into syllables? What is <u>broccoli</u>?

_____

- -

_____

2. Read the line below.

> She doesn't like cookies or caramel cake.

Circle the word <u>caramel</u>. Break it into syllables. Say each syllable. Put the word back together. Say the word again. What does <u>caramel</u> mean? You can use a dictionary to help you.

_____

- -

_____

3. Practice reading the poem aloud with expression. Then read it aloud to a partner. Listen to your partner read aloud. Tell your partner what was good about how he or she read. Tell one thing that could be better.

Assessment Practice   **Directions** Answer the questions based on the poem you just read.

1 **Read the line below.**

> She doesn't like pizza or <u>waffles</u> or steak.

Which of the following shows the correct way to break the word <u>waffles</u>?

A waff-les

B waf-fles

C waffl-es

D wa-ffles

2 **Read the line below.**

> Or custard or mustard or strawberry jam.

Which two words rhyme?

A <u>custard</u> and <u>mustard</u>

B <u>or</u> and <u>custard</u>

C <u>mustard</u> and <u>strawberry</u>

D <u>strawberry</u> and <u>jam</u>

Focus on California Content Standards

Lesson 7   Understand Synonym and Antonyms

Standard 2RW1.7   Understand and explain common antonyms and synonyms.

Synonyms are words that mean about the same as another word. Look at these synonyms:

happy	glad
little	small
shiny	bright

Read these sentences.

The fish is <u>little</u>.
The fish is <u>small</u>.

<u>Little</u> and <u>small</u> are synonyms. They mean about the same thing.

Antonyms are words that have opposite meanings. Look at these antonyms:

nice	mean
happy	sad
light	heavy

Look at these sentences.

This box is <u>light</u>.
This box is <u>heavy</u>.

<u>Light</u> and <u>heavy</u> mean the opposite.

Guided Reading Instruction

Directions Read the story below. Use the questions on the side to guide your reading. Then answer the questions. You may use a dictionary.

Weather Happens
by Audrey B. Baird

Guided Questions

1 It's still dark. I hear rain even before I wake. There goes the ride to the lake, the fishing, the picnic.

The phone rings. "Find your dad's rain poncho," says Grandpa. "It'll cover you right down to your toes."

We're still going? I pop on an extra sweater.

A ponchoed Grandpa honks and jumps from his car. **2** Dad gives him our cooler full of picnic.

"We'll eat in the car," says Grandpa with a wave. Mom shakes her head and smiles.

On the freeway, we drink hot chocolate from travel mugs. Windshield wipers beat time to the radio.

3 "COOL!" says Grandpa with a grin.

I hold up my cup. "Hot," I say, and we laugh.

Four boats on the lake. Grandpa looks skyward—loads our gear. I bail out the boat.

"You want to row?" asks Grandpa.

The oars are slippery. Rain drips off my nose. Steam rises up from the water.

Fat drops tap softly on our bait bucket. We bait our hooks and . . . wait.

1 Read the first sentence. Circle the word dark. What is an antonym for the word dark?

2 Read this sentence. Circle the word that means the opposite of empty.

3 Circle the word grin. What is another word that means about the same? Why does Grandpa grin?

"Good fishin' weather," Grandpa says. **4** His eyes crinkle from deep inside the poncho.

5 "GREAT!" I shout, pulling in the first fish.

We catch our limit before lunch and scarf Mom's picnic in the car.

Grandpa pulls out a thermos of soup and leans back. "Cool!" he says.

I hold up my cup. "Hot," I say, and we both laugh.

4 Circle the word crinkle. Crinkle means "crumple." What is another word that means about the same? It rhymes with crinkle. Why do you think Grandpa's eyes crinkle?

5 Circle the word that means the opposite of last.

1. Read this sentence.

> A ponchoed Grandpa honks and jumps from his car.

What is a synonym for jumps?

_____

- -

_____

2. Why is the ending of this story funny?

_____

- -

_____

_____

- -

_____

Apply   **Directions** Read the story below. Then answer the questions that follow. You may use a dictionary.

The Ocean is Big, My Father Said
by Linda Ward Stephens

"What's the ocean like?" I asked my father as he packed the car.

"The ocean is big," my father said. "A ship takes two weeks to cross it."

"What's the ocean like?" I asked my mother as she made sandwiches for our trip.

"The ocean is always moving," my mother said. "The tide goes in and out. The waves roll in forever."

"What is the ocean like?" I asked my brother and sister as we buckled our seat belts.

"The ocean is deep," my brother said, "and full of monsters. There are whales as big as our house and sharks as big as the car."

"The ocean is cold," my sister said, "and the water tastes like salt."

"Will I like it?" I asked. I really wanted to know.

"Oh yes!" said my father and mother.

"Of course," said my brother and sister.

I went down to the beach. I stared out at the ocean. My father was right, the ocean was big. It made me feel very small. My mother was right. The waves rolled in and in and in.

I waded into the water. One wave was so big it knocked me over.
I scrambled to my feet. My sister was right. The water was cold and salty.

Was my brother right, too? Were there monsters in the ocean?
I backed out and stood on the beach.

Nobody was right about one thing—I didn't like the ocean at all.
I walked away.

I found a pool filled with seawater. It was left behind when the
tide went out. The pool was not too big. It was not too deep. It was
not too cold. I waded in. Tiny fishes swam around my toes. There was
a starfish hiding in the rocks, and two little crabs were on the bottom.

It was a piece of the ocean just my size, and I liked it.

1. Read this sentence.

"The tide goes in and out."

Circle the two words that are antonyms. Can you think of two other
words that mean the same?

_____

- -

_____

2. Read this sentence.

My father was right, the ocean was <u>big</u>.

Name two synonyms for the word <u>big</u>. Pretend you are at the ocean.
Use one of the synonyms for big in a sentence of your own.

_____

- -

_____

- -

_____

3. Read this sentence

> It made me feel very <u>small</u>.

Name two synonyms for the word <u>small</u>. Why did the girl feel very small?

_____

- -

_____

_____

- -

_____

Assessment Practice   **Directions** Answer each question.

1 **Read this sentence.**

> "The ocean is <u>cold</u>," my sister said, "and the water tastes like salt."

Which word below is a synonym for <u>cold</u>?

A warm

B hot

C cool

D boiling

2 **Which word below is an antonym for <u>cold</u>?**

A hot

B icy

C cool

D crisp

Focus on California Content Standards

Lesson 8   **Understand Compound Words**

Standard 2RW1.8 Use knowledge of individual words in unknown compound words to predict their meaning.

Compound words are big words that are made up of two smaller words. Here are some compound words.

earthworm   waterfall   blackberry

Here's how you can figure out compound words you don't know. Look at this sentence.

Justin found an <u>earthworm</u> in the garden.

- First, divide the compound word. Make two smaller words.

    <u>earth</u> + <u>worm</u>

- Then think about what each word means.

    <u>Earth</u> means "ground."

    A <u>worm</u> is a small animal that lives in the ground.

- Next, add the meanings together. Use the meaning of each word to help you make up a definition.

    An <u>earthworm</u> is "a small animal that lives in the ground."

- Finally, make sure that your definition makes sense.

     Measuring Up® to the California Content Standards

Guided Reading Instruction

Directions Read the story below. Use the questions on the side to guide your reading

The Rainbow
by Abby Hawkins

Guided Questions

Carrie sat on a train bench with her sister Lydia. It was almost time to go. They were off to Gran's for the summer.

Carrie was very excited. Gran was a lot of fun. They had big plans for the summer. She was also excited because they were taking the train alone. This was the very first time. Carrie couldn't wait. Usually, her parents went with them, but this year the girls were going alone.

1 She checked her backpack one more time. She wanted to make sure that she had her sunglasses. The sun was very bright in the mountains. She checked the side pocket to make sure that she had her notebook. She liked to write notes about the scenes she saw along the way. **2** She checked another pocket to make sure that she had her new raincoat. Sometimes, there were big rainstorms in the mountains.

Carrie looked at her watch again. It was almost 2 o'clock. Just then, there was an announcement. "Everyone going to *Hot Springs, Cedar Falls,* and *Bear River,* Track 12," said the announcer.

Carrie and Lydia grabbed their backpacks and walked to Track 12. They found two good seats by a window. They took out a few snacks and some magazines. Carrie always bought her favorite magazines, but she never read them. She always stared out the window. This was her favorite part.

1 Circle the word <u>backpack</u>. What are the two smaller words? Tell what each word means. What does the word <u>backpack</u> mean?

2 Circle the word <u>raincoat</u>. What are the two smaller words? What does the word <u>raincoat</u> mean? Name another word that you can make from <u>rain</u>.

In a few minutes, the trains left the station. **3** Carrie loved traveling on the railroad. As the train sped along, she looked out the big window. Once they got out of the city, there was a lot of farmland. She liked to see the farm animals, but she really liked seeing the yellow sunflowers. There were miles and miles and miles of them. She liked the way the little faces pointed toward the sun. She thought it was funny how they all pointed in the same direction. She also liked the old farmhouses with their pretty flower boxes. She liked to imagine who lived there. Did they have children? **4** How far away was the schoolhouse? How did they get to school? What was it like to live on a farm? To Carrie, all the farmhouses seemed like they were in the middle of nowhere.

After a few hours of sunflowers and goats and cows, the train started its long climb. They had reached the mountains. This was Carrie's favorite part. About half way up, it started to rain. **5** At times, the raindrops were huge. They looked like big drops of ice. The storm lasted for about half an hour. By the time they got to Hot Springs, the rain had stopped. But it was still gray and cloudy. When they got to Cedar Falls, the sun was trying to come out. By the time they reached Bear River, they stepped off the train to see a big rainbow. It reached all the way across the sky. That's when Carrie knew this would be a very special vacation. Rainbows are very good luck! That's what Gran always told her.

Guided Questions

3 Circle the word railroad. What are the two smaller words? What is a railroad?

4 Find the compound word in this sentence. What are the two smaller words? What does this word mean? Name another compound word that can be made from the word house.

5 Find the compound word in this sentence. What does this word mean?

1. Read this sentence.

> She wanted to make sure that she had her <u>sunglasses</u>.

What does the word <u>sunglasses</u> mean? Why did Carrie bring her <u>sunglasses</u>?

_____

_____

_____

_____

2. Read this sentence.

> She checked the side pocket to make sure that she had her <u>notebook</u>.

What is a <u>notebook</u>? Why did Carrie take a notebook?

_____

_____

_____

_____

3. Read this sentence.

> Once they got out of city, there was a lot of farmland.

Circle the compound word in this sentence. How do you know which word is the compound word? What does it mean?

_____

_____

_____

_____

Apply   **Directions** Read the story below. Then answer the questions that follow.

The Case of the Missing Ice Cream
by Molly Myers

Buttercup chomped on purple wildflowers. She was upset. A few minutes ago, she'd wandered over to the barnyard to find Oscar. But he wasn't there. She saw his brother.

"Curly," she said. "Where's Oscar?"

"Well, he's not here," said Curly. "He's down by the pond. Thanks to the rainstorm last night there's a lot of mud."

"Curly, I really, really need to talk with him," Buttercup said seriously.

"Well, he's at the pond," replied Curly.

"Oscar, the last time I went to the pond, I got stuck," said Buttercup. "A muddy pond is NOT a good place for a cow, you know."

"Yuh, I know," laughed Curly. That had been quite a day. It had taken four horses to pull her out.

"Curly, I'm going over to the meadow. If you see Oscar, please tell him that I'm looking for him," said Buttercup.

"Okay, bye," said Curly.

Now she was eating wildflowers. She always ate wildflowers when she was upset. Buttercup did not know what to do. The ice cream was missing.

A while ago, she had looked in the ice shed. It was gone. She had noticed footprints in the dirt. But she didn't know whose feet they were.

This afternoon was her ice cream party. But now, no ice cream.

     Measuring Up® to the California Content Standards

"Hey, Buttercup," said Oscar.

"Oh, hi, Oscar," said Buttercup in a surprised voice. "I didn't hear you."

"What's wrong?" asked Oscar.

"A lot!" said Buttercup. "Someone has stolen all the ice cream."

"You're kidding, right?" asked Oscar. Buttercup knew that Oscar was the right animal to tell. He loved ice cream more than anyone in the yard. Oscar got grumpy, anytime he was without ice cream.

Oscar was very quiet for a few minutes. Then he said, " I bet someone buried it underwater in the stream."

"That's weird," said Buttercup. "Why would someone bury the ice cream in the stream?"

"The stream is very cold. It won't melt there," said Oscar.

"Let's go see if we can catch the thief!" said Oscar with a chuckle.

"Okay," said Buttercup. She didn't really want to stop eating wildflowers, but she knew that Oscar needed her company.

It was a nice day. Buttercup and Oscar had a lively chat as they walked along a narrow footpath. It was almost too narrow for the two of them. The sunshine felt good on her back.

It took them about five minutes. They walked downhill past the beehive. Buttercup moved a little faster. She didn't like bees.

A short time later they arrived.

"Let's stop right here and wait," said Oscar. "I bet that whoever it is will show up soon."

"It's still daytime, Oscar. Won't they wait until it gets dark?" asked Buttercup.

"No, who wants to look for ice cream in the dark!" said Oscar laughing.

"That's a good point," said Buttercup. Buttercup thought Oscar was so smart.

A few minutes later, there was a sound.

"Buttercup, I think we have our thief!" whispered Oscar.

They peeked around the trunk of the willow tree. It was Cooper.

"It's Cooper," whispered Buttercup. "I can't believe it."

"Well, let's see what he does. Maybe he's just here to take a swim," said Oscar.

Oscar is always so fair, thought Buttercup. No one in the yard was more fair. They watched. First, Cooper drank some water. Then he went for a swim. Then he ate a few blueberries. Then he looked around. Buttercup grabbed Oscar's tail and pulled it. It was very difficult to not talk.

 Measuring Up® to the California Content Standards

Cooper waddled over to some rocks in the stream. He started picking up pebbles. Soon, pebbles were flying everywhere. Then Cooper picked up a huge container of ice cream and put it on a nearby rock.

"That's enough, Cooper," yelled Oscar. Oscar was so brave, Buttercup thought.

"Ohhhhhhh!" screamed Cooper. "Why did you frighten me?"

"Why? You stole the ice cream," yelled Oscar.

"No, that's not true. I did not. All the ice in the shed started to melt. I moved it here until the party," said Cooper. "That's the truth. I don't even like ice cream."

"Oh," said Buttercup. "How nice of you, Cooper, but why didn't you tell me?"

"I couldn't find you," said Cooper.

"Well," said Oscar, "that's solved. Let's go for a swim before the party."

Buttercup thought Oscar was the most wonderful pig in the yard.

1. Read the sentence below.

> Buttercup chomped on purple wildflowers.

Circle the compound word in this sentence. What two smaller words make up this word? What does the compound word mean?

_____

- -

_____

_____

- -

_____

2. Read the sentence below.

> "Thanks to the rainstorm last night there's a lot of mud."

What two smaller words make up the compound word in this sentence? What does the compound word mean? Think of another word that can be made from <u>rain</u> or <u>storm</u>.

_____

- -

_____

_____

- -

_____

3. What did Buttercup notice in the dirt? What does this word mean? Who made the <u>footprints</u>?

_____

- -

_____

_____

- -

_____

Assessment Practice   **Directions** Answer the questions based on the story you just read.

1 <u>Barnyard</u> is a compound word. You can tell from the two parts of the word that a barnyard is

A a building where animals live.

B the inside of a barn.

C an area around a barn.

D the length of a barn.

2 **Read these sentences.**

Buttercup and Oscar had a lively chat as they walked along a narrow <u>footpath</u>.

What is a <u>footpath</u>?

A a very wide path to run along

B a narrow path to walk along

C one foot

D a highway

A **prefix** is one or more letters that you add to the beginning of a **root word.** A prefix changes the meaning of the word. Here are some prefixes.

over-	too much	overdo
re-	again	remake
un-	not, do the reverse of	unlike

A **suffix** is one or more letters that you add at the end of a root word. Here are some suffixes.

-ful	full of	playful
-able	is, can be	agreeable
-ly	in a certain way	sadly

Sometimes a word ends in y. Change the y to i before you add -ly. For example, if you wanted to add -ly to the word angry, you would change the y to i to make the word angrily.

Sometimes a word ends in e. Drop the e before adding -able. For example, if you wanted to add -able to the word love, you would drop the e before adding -able to make the word lovable.

The letters -ing are a very special verb ending.

They cry.
They are crying.

Guided Reading Instruction

Directions Read the story below. Use the questions on the side to guide your reading.

The Boogie Board
by Djeema Jensen

1 Scotty and Willis sneaked quickly up the attic steps. They didn't want anyone to hear them. Scotty wanted to find his birthday present. He knew that he shouldn't do this, but he HAD to. He really, really wanted a boogie board. He couldn't wait two more days to find out.

"You know that we shouldn't be up here, Scotty," whispered Willis. "Your mom will be very unhappy if she finds out."

2 "I know, but she won't be home for awhile, and Dad's writing in his office. I just have to find it. I can't wait even one more day," said Scotty.

"What are you going to do if you find it? **3** Are you going to unwrap it?" asked Willis.

"Yup! I want to see if it's a *Speedster.* Then I'm going to rewrap it. No one will ever know, but you!" laughed Scotty.

"I'm sure that it's in here. This is where my mom puts all the presents," said Scotty. He was looking inside a huge old trunk. But Scotty didn't see one present. He closed the top very quietly.

"I can't believe this! I wonder where she put it?" asked Scotty.

"I don't know," said Willis.

4 "You're so helpful," laughed Scotty. Scotty was looking under a pile of old clothes now.

"Scotty, don't unfold those clothes. Your mom will notice," said Willis seriously. "C 'mon, it's time to go the beach. Can't we just go now? Your dad said he'd take us whenever we want to go."

1 Circle the word that means "fast." What is the root word? What is the suffix? Why did the boys sneak <u>quickly</u> up the stairs?

2 Circle the word that tells what dad is doing. What is the ending?

3 Circle the word in this sentence that has a prefix that means "do the reverse of." Use this word in a sentence of your own.

4 Circle the word in this sentence that means "willing to help." What is one way to be <u>helpful</u> at home? Use <u>helpful</u> in your answer.

"In a minute," said Scotty. "The board must be up here. It's not as if it's a little present."

"Wow, look at this old book about pirates!" said Willis. **5** "It's from the library, and it's way overdue. It was due July 29, 1990! He renewed it five times. I bet your dad took out this book when he was writing that story about pirates. I wonder why he didn't return it?"

"I don't know," said Scotty. He didn't really care right now. He was looking in the closet. This was where his mom kept all the old sports equipment. He felt like taking every last item out of the closet, it was such a mess. **6** The only problem was that he knew that it would take hours to rearrange everything.

"C'mon Scotty, let's go! I want to go body surf," said Willis. "Are you going to unpack every box in this attic? What's happened to my most likable friend? You're my friend who loves to surf more than anyone I know. You're my friend who likes to have fun! This is boring! I want to go to the beach."

"Okay! Okay! Let's go! I guess they didn't get me a boogie board after all," said Scotty sadly. "How boring is that?"

"Too boring! But, Scotty, there are two more days until your birthday. Just because it's not up here, doesn't mean that you're not getting it," said Willis.

"Maybe you're right," said Scotty. "Okay, let's go body surf. I hope there are some good waves today!"

Guided Questions

5 Read this sentence. What does it mean when a book is <u>overdue</u>?

6 Circle the word in the sentence that has a prefix that means "again." What would take hours for Scotty to put back in place?

1. Read this sentence.

> He closed the top very <u>quietly</u>.

What is the root word in <u>quietly</u>? What is the suffix? What does the root word mean? What does <u>quietly</u> mean?

_____

- -

_____

- -

_____

2. What has Scotty's father <u>renewed</u> five times? Use this word in your answer.

_____

- -

_____

3. Read this sentence.

> "What's happened to my most <u>likable</u> friend?"

<u>Like</u> means "to enjoy someone or something." What does the suffix <u>-able</u> mean? What does <u>likable</u> mean? Name someone or something you find likable?

_____

- -

_____

- -

_____

- -

_____

Apply

Directions Read the story below. Then answer the questions that follow.

The Story of the Big Yellow Bird
by Christy Gilbert

"Hey, Jen, it's almost time to meet Rosie," said Tung. "Remember, today is the kite festival. We told Jen we'd meet her at 12 noon."

"I'm almost ready. I want to mail this letter to my pen pal. I just have one more line to rewrite," said Jen.

"Okay!" said Tung. He looked across the street at the park. It was a beautiful spring day. The leaves on the trees were blowing gently. He hoped the breeze was strong enough to fly kites. By the time the contest started, maybe the wind would pick up a bit.

"Tung, I'm bringing my kite. It's over by the chair. The string is all tangled. Maybe you could untangle the string and then rewind it."

"Sure," said Tung in a cheerful voice. He walked over and began to unfold the kite. It was a giant yellow bird, and it was beautiful. There were little painted flowers on its wings. Its tail had six long blue streamers.

"This is the most beautiful kite, Jen. Where did you get it?" Tung asked.

"It was my grandmother's kite. She gave it to me last year. Her father made it for her when she was a little girl in Vietnam," answered Jen. "It's very special. Grandma thinks that I should repaint some of the flowers, but I like them just the way they are. They were painted long ago by my great grandfather."

Jen continued softly, " When she was about ten, she won a very big kite contest with this kite. I can't tell you how many times she's told me the story. I make her retell it every time she visits. It's a good luck kite, and I hope it brings me luck today!"

"I hope so, too, Jen," said Tung, as he undid the last knot in the string.

"Thanks for being so thoughtful," said Jen. "I couldn't believe how many knots were in the string when I looked at it this morning."

"No problem," said Tung. He looked carefully at the string again. He wanted to make sure that he didn't overlook any of the knots. When he was sure that he had untied all the knots, he started to rewind the string.

"Okay, I'm ready. Let's go fly this yellow bird," said Jen.

"All right. I think today is going to be your good-luck, fly-a-kite day!" laughed Tung.

"I hope so, I really hope so," said Jen.

1. Read the sentence below.

> Maybe you could untangle the string and then rewind it.

Circle the word that means "to remove knots." Name something that you have to untangle sometimes? Use <u>untangle</u> in your answer.

_____

- -

_____

_____

- -

_____

2. Read the sentence below.

> It was a giant yellow bird, and it was beautiful.

What does <u>beautiful</u> mean? Name something that you think is beautiful. Use <u>beautiful</u> in your answer.

_____

- -

_____

_____

- -

_____

_____

- -

_____

3. Read the sentence below.

> "Thanks for being so thoughtful," said Jen.

What does <u>thoughtful</u> mean in this sentence? Why does Jen think Tung is thoughtful?

_____

- -

_____

_____

- -

_____

_____

- -

_____

Assessment Practice

Directions Answer each question below about the story you just read.

1 **Read the sentence below.**

> The leaves on the trees were blowing gently.

Which of the following words means "gently"?

A not loudly

B not kindly

C not roughly

D not angrily

2 **When you <u>overlook</u> something, you**

A notice it.

B don't notice it.

C hide it.

D give it away.

Sometimes two words are spelled alike but have different meanings. Look at these words and their meanings.

tick	clicking sound a clock makes
tick	a tiny insect that bites
squash	a vegetable
squash	to flatten

You will come across words like these in your reading. This is what you can do to find out what meaning to use. Look at how the word is used in the sentence. Look at the other words in the sentence. They can help you figure out what the word means.

Read this sentence.

Our class is growing <u>squash</u> and pumpkins in our school garden.

<u>Pumpkins</u> and <u>garden</u> are also in this sentence. You know that pumpkins grow in a garden. These words can help you figure out that <u>squash</u> means "a vegetable" in this sentence.

Guided Reading Instruction

Directions Read the following story. Use the questions on the side to guide your reading. Then answer the questions that follow.

Petunia's Secret
By Darcy Brown

"What's all that noise?" yelled Mr. Gomez to Miguel. "Petunia is making a big racket."

"She sure is," said Miguel. "I'll go look."

Pedro ran down to the pond. By the time he got there, the noise had stopped. **1** He saw Petunia. She was gliding back and forth in the water. He looked around. He didn't see anything strange. He listened. He didn't hear anything strange. Petunia only made a lot of noise when an animal was getting too close to her ducklings. But Miguel didn't see any ducklings. In fact, Miguel was worried. It was spring. By this time, Petunia always had a new family.

He headed back up to the house.

"See anything?" asked Mr. Gomez. Mr. Gomez ran the ranch for Miguel's father. He was also Miguel's' best pal. Miguel had known him all his life. He taught Miguel all about animals. That's all Miguel cared about—animals, animals, animals. Mr. Gomez always said that Miguel was his very best pupil at his "Animal School"! He was also his only pupil!

2 "Mr. Gomez, what's the date today?" asked Miguel.

"It's the third of May," said Mr. Gomez. "Why?"

"Well, I don't think there are any ducklings," said Miguel. "Don't you think it's strange? Petunia was floating around in the pond catching flies. I didn't see any ducklings. If there were new ducklings, she'd be at her nest, right?"

Guided Questions

1 Circle the word <u>saw</u>. <u>Saw</u> can mean a "tool that cuts wood." Is that what it means in this sentence? What does <u>saw</u> mean in this sentence?

2 Read the next two sentences. Circle the word in this sentence that means "a certain, day, month, and year." What is the <u>date</u> in the story? What else can <u>date</u> mean?

" Most likely," said Mr. Gomez. "Maybe she's hiding them. Give her some more time."

"Okay, but the science fair is in a month. I want to do a report on ducks, and I want to take two ducklings," said Miguel.

"I'm sure there will be ducklings," said Mr. Gomez. "Have you fed Big Red? I noticed that his bowl was empty."

"No, I haven't even seen Big Red," said Miguel. "I wonder where he is? **3** I haven't even heard a bark from him today."

"He's most likely in the yard. It's a sunny day. He likes the sun," said Mr. Gomez. "I bet that he's right next to his bowl just waiting for you!"

"Okay, I'll go feed him. See you later," said Miguel, laughing. "Big Red lives to eat!"

"Right," said Mr. Gomez.

Miguel walked up to the house. Big Red was nowhere to be found. This is very strange, thought Miguel. He poured some dry food into Big Red's bowl. Then he walked over to the porch. He sat down in his favorite chair.

He picked up a new book. He'd just found it at the library. **4** It was all about how to raise rabbits.

In a few minutes, he'd forgotten all about Big Red and Petunia. He'd even forgotten about ducklings. About ten minutes later, he heard a big fuss. There were woof, woof, woofs. There were quack, quack, quacks. There were peep, peep, peeps! He looked up. First, he saw Big Red. He was prancing across the yard. Behind him was Petunia. She was quacking wildly and flapping her wings. Behind Petunia, there were eight ducklings. **5** They were all lined up in a row. And following right behind was Mr. Gomez.

Guided Questions

3 Circle the word that means "noise a dog makes." What is another meaning for this word?

4 Circle the word raise. Raise can mean "to lift up or to move up higher." It can also mean "to help young animals grow up." What is the meaning in this sentence?

5 Circle the word row. What is the meaning of row in this sentence? Use the other meaning of row in a sentence of your own.

Miguel jumped out of his chair. He started running toward them. What a parade! It was the best parade that he'd ever seen. He couldn't stop smiling!

"Wow!" yelled Miguel. "What a great surprise!"

"Sure is," said Mr. Gomez. "Petunia really knows how to keep a secret, doesn't she?"

"She sure does," Miguel said, laughing. "She sure does."

1. Read these sentences.

> It was spring. By this time, Petunia always had a new family.

Underline the word that means "the season after winter." What usually happens at the ranch at this time of year?

_____

2. Read this sentence.

> "Petunia was just floating around in the pond catching <u>flies</u>."

One meaning of <u>flies</u> is "travels through the air." What is the meaning of <u>flies</u> in this sentence?

_____

3. Read this sentence.

> "I bet that he's right next to his bowl just waiting for you!"

Circle the word that can mean "deep dish" or "game played with a ball and pins." Then write a sentence for each meaning.

_____

_____

 Measuring Up® to the California Content Standards

Apply   **Directions** Read the following story. Then answer the questions that follow.

Stoop Stories

By Stephanie Brown Owens

Jackson and Kayla were sitting on the stoop. They called it the story stoop. It was a good place to sit and watch the world go by. It was also a very good place to wait for Mr. Nicholas. Mr. Nicholas told great stories. He was also a famous writer, but Jackson and Kayla hadn't read his books. They were grown-up books.

Anyhow, he lived next door. He had lived in the same apartment for sixty years. Yes, sixty years. That's what he told them. He liked to tell them that he'd seen small trees grow very tall. He also liked to tell them about the tree in front of his building. It seems he'd planted it about 35 years ago. Now he could see the top of it from his apartment window. Just a week ago, he'd watched it pop little green buds. He loved the color of those little green buds. He always said the color of spring was green, and it's the prettiest green in the whole world. "Puts me in a story-telling mood," he'd say. Then he'd laugh a big laugh.

He'd also seen small children grow tall. Those children now had their own children. That's how he knew Jackson and Kayla. Their mom had grown up in the neighborhood and listened to his stories.

"Where do you think Mr. Nicholas is today?" asked Kayla. "It's late. He's never late. He always takes his afternoon walk at 3 o'clock."

"Stop worrying, Kayla," said Jackson. "He'll show up when he shows up."

Kayla took a big swallow of lemonade so she wouldn't talk. She didn't like it when Jackson said, "He'll show up when he shows up."

"Well, I'm tired of waiting. I really want to know if Zachary got away from the swamp monster. Can you imagine getting lost in a swamp? It must be awful, awful, awful! I've never even seen a swamp. There are crocodiles in swamps, right? I bet there are animals that fly through the air, too."

"Yeah, right" said Jackson. Sometimes his sister drove him crazy. Why was she so worried about a dumb swamp? It's not like they were going to a swamp anytime soon.

"Kayla, it's just a story that Mr. Nicholas made up. You know where he grew up. He's told you one hundred times. Everyone in his town made up scary swamp stories. They even had contests. Maybe that's why he's a famous writer."

"Oh, look, Jackson, there's a swallow," said Kayla pointing across the street. "It just flew under Mrs. Flanigan's roof. I wonder if there's a nest."

Jackson and Kayla were so busy talking they didn't hear Mr. Nicholas arrive.

"Hi, kids! What's going on?" said Mr. Nicholas.

"Hi, Mr. Nicholas!" said Jackson and Kayla. "How are you today?"

"Just fine," Mr. Nicholas replied. "Ready for the rest of the story?"

"YES!" they both yelled.

"Well, it's pretty short. Zachary spent the night in a tree. He was too scared to stay on the ground. He was afraid the night monster might get him. He didn't sleep a wink. The night sounds never stopped. There were hoots, and yells, and screeches, and howls. At one point, he even heard something scratching on the bark of the tree. He didn't think daylight would ever come.

"When it finally did, Zachary scooted down that tree as fast as he could. He found a little boat nearby. He jumped in that boat and started to row. He wasn't sure where he was going, but he didn't care. He rowed and rowed. Finally, he got to the lake where he could see his house. Now if he could just get across the lake."

"But, Mr. Nicholas, what happened to the night monster?" asked Kayla.

"Oh, Kayla, there wasn't really a night monster. It was all in Zachary's imagination. The moonlight made a big shadow on the trees. The shadow looked like a monster," said Mr. Nicholas.

"Oh," said Kayla.

"Okay, well, what happens next?" asked Jackson.

"Well, that's another story for another day!" said Mr. Jackson. "I'll see you tomorrow."

"Oh, Mr. Nicholas, that's not fair," squealed Kayla.

1. Read these sentences.

> Jackson and Kayla were sitting on the <u>stoop</u>. They called it the story stoop.

One meaning of <u>stoop</u> is "to bend over." Circle the word that tells what a <u>stoop</u> means in this sentence. Why do Kayla and Jackson like to sit on the <u>stoop</u>?

_____

_____

_____

_____

2. Read this sentence.

> Kayla took a big <u>swallow</u> of lemonade so she wouldn't talk.

<u>Swallow</u> means "a gulp of food or liquid" or "a bird." What does <u>swallow</u> mean in this sentence. What word helps you? Circle it.

_____

- -

_____

- -

_____

3. Read this sentence.

> He jumped in that boat and started to <u>row</u>.

What word helps you figure out what <u>row</u> means in this sentence? Circle it. Why did Zachary start to <u>row</u>?

_____

- -

_____

- -

_____

Assessment Practice

Directions Answer each question below about the story you just read.

1 **Read this sentence.**

> Now he could see the <u>top</u> of it from his apartment window.

In which sentence below does <u>top</u> have the same meaning?

A Neena bought a toy <u>top</u> for her little brother.

B They were almost at the <u>top</u> of the mountain.

C That <u>top</u> spins better than this one!

D I don't know how to make this <u>top</u> work.

2 **Read this sentence.**

> "Oh, Mr. Nicholas, that's not fair," squealed Kayla.

In which sentence does fair have the same meaning?

A Antonio and Hannah went to the <u>fair</u>.

B Sierra played a lot of different games at the <u>fair</u>.

C Sadie doesn't think those rules are <u>fair</u>.

D Last year at the <u>fair</u> we rode on the ferris wheel.

Read this selection. Then answer the questions that follow it.

Jazz-Ma-Tazz
By Lindy Hansen

Today is MY jazz-ma-tazz day! "Come on, David," calls my mom.

I hurry and gather up my music books. We drive all the way across town.

"Did you practice?" asks my mom.

I nod, then give her my famous jack-o'-lantern grin. The car climbs slowly up the steep hill.

"Have a good lesson," she says. I slam the car door and wave.

I race up the steps two at a time. *Jazz-ma-tazz! Jazz-ma-tazz!* my heart sings.

My piano teacher opens the front door. "Hello, David," she says. "It's your turn."

I smile. My piano teacher has pink hair.

"What did you like best this week?" she asks.

Proudly I show her my jazz book. It has wild patterns on the front.

"Should we play it first? Or save it for dessert?" she asks.

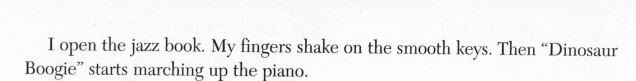

I open the jazz book. My fingers shake on the smooth keys. Then "Dinosaur Boogie" starts marching up the piano.

"Bravo," says the pink-haired lady.

My hands are happy now. I play "Pizza Blue." And "Turtle Blues." And "Crazy Day Waltz."

"My, my!" says my teacher. "You've practiced a lot."

On and on I play. *Jazz-ma-tazz! Jazz-ma-tazz!* sings my heart.

"Best lesson ever!" laughs my teacher.

Then she turns the page. "Now we'll try the chords," she says. "Can you hear them?"

I close my eyes. I hear two sounds . . . no, three sounds at once! It's wonderful!

My teacher smiles. "Watch me, David," she says. "Copy my fingers."

My hands ease onto the keys. The magic begins. I work hard.

"Here's the best part," says my teacher. She plays "Turtle Blues" and the chords at the same time!

Jazz-ma-tazz! Jazz-ma-tazz! sings my heart. I can add all these sounds to my songs!

We work and we work. I count and I play. We even play "Wildcat Walk" together.

"Oh my," says my teacher. "We're out of time. Don't forget to practice." As if I could!

"Good-bye, David," calls the pink-haired lady.

I give her my famous jack-o'-lantern grin. "Jazz-ma-tazz!" I say.

1 Read the sentence below.

> I <u>count</u> and I play.

Which word has the same vowel sound as <u>count</u>?

A sound

B door

C nod

D smooth

2 Read the sentence below.

> I nod, then give her my famous jack-o'-lantern grin.

Which of the following shows the correct way to break <u>famous</u>?

A fam-ous

B fa-mous

C f-amous

D famo-us

3 Read the sentence below.

> Then "<u>Dinosaur</u> Boogie" starts marching up the piano.

The vowel in the first syllable of <u>dinosaur</u> sounds like the vowel in

A bin.

B kind.

C hit.

D miss

4 **Suppose David has a piano lesson on Saturday, July 9. What is the correct abbreviation for this date?**

A Sat Jul 9

B Sat. Jul 9

C Sat., Jul. 9

D Satur., Jul. 9

5 Read this sentence.

> My piano <u>teacher</u> opens the front door.

What is the correct way to write the plural of <u>teacher</u>?

A teacheres

B teacheress

C teacherss

D teachers

6 **Which two words from the story have the same vowel sound?**

A <u>chords</u> and <u>sounds</u>

B <u>good</u> and <u>door</u>

C <u>sings</u> and <u>pink</u>

D <u>save</u> and <u>hands</u>

7 **Read the sentence below.**

"Here's the <u>best</u> part," says my teacher.

Which word below is an antonym for <u>best</u>?

A worst

B finest

C greatest

D wonderful

8 **Read the sentence below.**

We even play "<u>Wildcat</u> Walk" together.

What is a <u>wildcat</u>?

A a cat who likes to dance

B a small cat that is not tame, such as a bobcat

C a silly cat

D a cat that is tame

9 **Read this sentence.**

The car climbs slowly up the hill.

How does car move when it moves slowly?

A The car moves very fast.

B The car stops and does not move.

C The car does not move fast.

D The car speeds along.

10 **Read this sentence.**

I slam the car door and <u>wave</u>.

In which sentence below does <u>wave</u> have the same meaning?

A "Be careful that <u>wave</u> doesn't hit you!" yelled Raphael.

B "Let's ride the next wave that comes in," said Kyra.

C "We haven't had one good wave today," says Andrew.

D "Don't forget to wave!" said Mrs. Maguire.

Focus on California Content Standards

Standard 2RW2.1 Use titles, table of contents, and chapter headings to locate information in expository text.

When you read, it is important to understand the parts of a book. These parts can help you find information.

Here are four important parts of a book.

- **Title** A title is the name of a book. It usually gives you the topic of the book.

- **Table of Contents** The table of contents helps you know what information can be found in the book. It lists the chapter headings. It will tell you where to find special information about the topic.

- **Chapter Title** A chapter title tells you the name of each chapter. The chapter titles are always in order. A book may have many chapters. Next to the name of each new chapter, you will see the page number where that chapter begins.

You can see how many pages a chapter is by looking at where the next chapter begins. For example, look at these chapter titles.

Desert Trees	35
Desert Flowers	39

You know that the chapter about Desert Trees begins on page 35 and a chapter about Desert Flowers begins on page 39. You can figure out that the chapter about Desert Trees is four pages. This helps you to figure out how much information the book has about different desert trees.

- **Chapter Headings** Some books have chapter headings. Chapter headings are listed under the Chapter titles. They tell you what information can be found in a chapter.

Guided Reading Instruction

Directions Read the following table of contents. Use the questions on the side to guide your reading. Then answer the questions that follow.

This is a table of contents for a book named *The Joshua Tree Desert*.

Guided Questions

1 Table of Contents

1 You know the title of this book is *The Joshua Tree Desert*. Look over the table of contents. What information is in this book?

2 What is the topic of the first chapter? On what page does this chapter begin?

3 On which pages would you find information about mountain sheep?

4 On what page does Chapter 3 begin? What is the chapter title? What are the chapter headings in this chapter?

5 What pictures would you expect to see?

1. How many chapters are in *The Joshua Tree Desert?*

- -

_____

2. On what pages does information about jack rabbits begin?

- -

_____

3. How do you know what information will be in chapter 2? Do you think there will be information about birds in chapter 2? Explain.

- -

_____

- -

_____

- -

_____

4. If you were reading page 24, what information would you be reading?

- -

_____

5. What is at the very end of the book? On which page does it start?

- -

_____

Apply **Directions** Read the article below. Then answer the questions that follow.

Desert Tortoises
by Lily Yellowbird

There are some very old creatures in California. That's right! Land turtles have been around a long time. Today there aren't as many left. That's why the state works hard to protect them. You cannot take a tortoise away from the desert. It is against the law.

Facts About Tortoises

Here are some facts you might like to know about these creatures.

- They are reptiles.
- They live on land.
- Most of the time they live under the ground.
- They like to eat a lot. They like weeds and dandelions.
- They also like wildflowers and different kinds of grasses.
- They weigh between 8 and 15 pounds.
- They are between 9 and 15 inches long.
- They have brown shells.
- They can live up to 100 years.
- From November until March, they stay in their burrows.

Be Nice to Tortoises

If you ever see a tortoise in the desert, be nice. That means it's okay to walk (not run) over to the tortoise. Let it see you so it doesn't get frightened. Take a close look. But don't touch it. Don't pick it up. Don't poke it with a stick. Don't take it home. Just take a good look. Then walk away quietly.

Remember that this creature has been around a long time. If people keep protecting them, they will be around for a lot longer.

1. What is the title of this article? What does the title help you know?

_____

_____

_____

_____

_____

2. In which of these books might you find this article?

> *Land Turtles*
> *Sea Turtles*
> *All About Birds*

_____

_____

3. Look at these chapters in a book. Which chapter would most likely have information about tortoises?

> Chapter 1: Honeypot Ants
> Chapter 2: Desert Scorpions
> Chapter 3: Where Tortoises Live

_____

_____

4. Look at these chapters in a book. Where would you find more information about what tortoises like to eat?

> Chapter 8: Who Lives in the Desert Willow Tree?
> Chapter 9: Do Tortoises Like Dandelions?
> Chapter 10: What Are Honeypot Ants?

_____

- -

_____

Assessment Practice   **Directions** Answer each question about the article you just read.

Here is a table of contents for a book about deserts in California. Use it to answer questions 1 and 2.

1 If you were reading page 12, which chapter are you reading?

A Chapter 2

B Chapter 6

C Chapter 3

D Chapter 5

2 Under which chapter heading would you most likely find information about where pupfish live?

A Wildflowers

B Desert Grasses

C Where Pupfish Live

D What Pupfish Look Like

Focus on California Content Standards

Lesson 12 Set Your Purpose for Reading

Standard 2RC2.2 State the purpose in reading (i.e., tell what information is sought).

Before you read a story or article, set a **purpose.** Decide why are you are reading.

Before you start to read, look at the book. Read the title. Look at the names of each chapter title. If there are headings, look at the name of each heading. Look at all the pictures. It will help you know what information is in the book.

If you are reading an article, look at the title. Look at the headings. Look at the pictures.

Pay attention to these parts of books and articles. They can help you state your purpose for reading.

Guided Reading Instruction

Directions Read the following article. Use the questions on the side to guide your reading. Then answer the questions that follow.

1 Traveling on Water

by Marilyn Kratz

People have always used boats of one kind or another. Long ago, hunters used them for fishing and for crossing rivers. Today, people use many kinds of boats for many different reasons.

Canoes

Canoes have been used for a long, long time. 2 Indians once used the bark of trees to make canoes. Today, canoes are made of wood or metal. One person sits in the front. The other person sits in the back. They dip their paddles in the water and push the water. This makes the canoe move forward. Some people use canoes for fishing on lakes. Other people use them just for fun.

Guided Questions

1 Read the title. Look at the headings. Why would you read this article?

2 For what did Indians use the bark of trees?

Sailboats

3 Sailboats use the wind to move. The wind blows against the sail. This makes the boat move through the water. Sailboats come in all sizes. Some are very large. They might have many sails. Some are very small. They are made for only one person to sail. Sailboats are mostly used for fun. But sometimes, people use them for fishing.

3 Read this sentence and the next. How do sailboats move?

4 Cargo Ships

Cargo ships carry different items all over the world. They carry food and clothes from one country to another. They carry furniture. They even carry cars and trucks. These items are unloaded from the ship at docks in big cities. Then, the items are put on trucks or railroads so they can go to different places. Some clothes you wear might have come to this country in a cargo ship.

4 Why should you read this section of the article?

Ocean Liners

Ocean liners carry people across the ocean. They are like huge floating hotels. Passengers eat in ship restaurants. They can go to the movies. They can swim in swimming pools.

5 Tugboats

Tugboats push large ships out to sea. When an ocean liner leaves a city, tugboats get on each side of the ship. They push against the ship and move it away from the dock. Then they help guide the ship as it sails out to the ocean.

5 What information is in this part of the article?

1. Name one new idea that you learned about canoes.

2. Name one new idea that you learned about cargo ships.

3. Name one new idea that you learned about ocean liners.

4. Name one new idea that you learned about tugboats.

Apply   **Directions** Read this article. Then answer the questions that follow.

How We Measure Things
by Darwin James

We use tools to measure things. We measure things to find out how big they are. We measure things to find out how heavy they are. Trucks can be very long. Other things, such as your shoes are not very big. An elephant can be very heavy. A penny is not very heavy.

Rulers

You can use rulers to measure how tall or long something is. You can use a ruler to find out how tall you are. You can use a ruler to measure how wide a door is. You can also use a ruler to measure how long a piece of ribbon is.

The ruler you use in school or at home is often one foot long. The ruler will also be marked off into twelve inches. The writing paper you use in school is often eleven inches from top to bottom.

Yardsticks

A yardstick is another kind of ruler. A yardstick is three feet long. People use yardsticks to measure things that are longer than one foot. An older person might use a yardstick to find out how tall a bookcase is. You and your classmates might also use a yardstick to measure the length and width of your classroom.

Scales

What if you wanted to know how heavy your backpack is? You would not use a ruler or a yardstick. You would use a scale. A scale tells how many pounds something weighs. You can weigh apples, books, and even your cat. You have probably stepped on a scale in a doctor's office or at home.

Other Measures

   How long or tall things are and how heavy they are are just a few
of the things that people measure. If you were making pudding, you
would need to know how much milk to use. You would use a
measuring cup. If you were in a race, you would need to know how
fast you ran. You would use a clock. Clocks measure time. If you want
to wear shorts and a T-shirt, you would use a thermometer.
Thermometers measure temperature.

1. What are some reasons people measure?

_____

_____

_____

_____

2. When do you use a ruler to measure?

_____

_____

_____

_____

3. What are some items that you can weigh on a scale?

_____

_____

_____

_____

4. What measuring tool would you use to measure milk?

_____

- -

_____

5. Complete the chart. Write the names of two measuring tools. Then name two items you could measure using that tool.

Name of Measuring Tool	Item to Measure

Assessment Practice   **Directions** Answer the questions based on the article you just read.

1 Which is the BEST purpose for reading this article?

A to read a funny story about measuring tools

B to find out more about measuring tools

C to find out how to use a stopwatch

D to find out how to make pudding

2 For which of the following would you use a yardstick to measure?

A pencil

B feather

C length of a room

D note paper

Focus on California Content Standards

Lesson 13 — Identify the Author's Purpose for Reading

Standard 2RC2.2   Use knowledge of the author's purpose to comprehend informational text.

Authors always have a reason why they write something. This is called the **author's purpose.** Here are some of the reasons.

- **An author wants to give you information about a topic.**
  An author writes an article about whales and includes a lot of facts. You learn more about whales when you read the article.

- **An author wants to tell you about something he or she cares about. The author wants you to care about this topic, too.**
  An author hears that her town library must close. The author does not want the library to close. So, she writes a story with a lot of reasons for keeping the library open. It is printed in the town newspaper. You read the story and learn why the author cares about the library. You want the library to stay open, too.

- **An author wants to explain how to make something or how to do something.**
  An author writes instructions about how to make a kite. It contains steps to follow. It may also have pictures that show how to do the steps. You learn how to make a kite when you read the article.

Guided Reading Instruction

Directions Read the following article. Use the questions on the side to guide your reading.

1 How To Plant a Butterfly Garden
by Lucy Owens

It's really fun to plant a butterfly garden. I know because it's my favorite kind of garden to plant. It also helps nature. 2 A garden will help to keep places for wildlife to live. You can make your own backyard a friendly place for butterflies. If you plant the right flowers, many butterflies will come to visit. You'll be able to watch them up close.

Here's what you can do to plant a butterfly garden.

3 First decide what size to make your garden. It can be a small garden in your backyard. Or, it can be a flower box in a window. Once you decide where to plant your butterfly garden, follow these steps.

Guided Questions

1 What is the purpose of this article?

2 Read the next two sentences. How will a butterfly garden help nature?

3 What is the first decision that you have to make?

- Do a little bit of research. Find out what butterflies live in your area. Choose a warm day. Ask a family member to take a walk with you. Take a butterfly walk. Go to a nearby park. Or go to a public garden. Sit down for a while. Look for butterflies. When you see one, make a few notes. Look it up in a butterfly book later.

- Find out the names of different flowers that bloom in your area. You want flowers that bloom from spring to fall. The flowers will provide nectar for the butterflies. Nectar is sweet liquid. It is inside a flower. This is what butterflies like to eat.

- Choose flowers that are bright. **4** Butterflies like very colorful flowers. Their favorite colors are red, yellow, orange, and purple. You might want to plant marigolds, zinnias or purple asters.

4 Why is it important to plant colorful flowers?

- Plant your garden. As the plants grow, do not use any bad sprays to keep bugs away. These sprays will hurt the butterflies. Water your garden as needed.

- When the flowers bloom, spend time in your garden. Butterflies are not really afraid of humans, so you can watch them up close. Butterflies like warm days. **5** That's when you'll see them sucking nectar. If it's a cool day, you might catch them sunning themselves on a rock. After it rains, you might see them "puddling." This is when they suck water from the ground.

5 Why do butterflies like warm days?

- Take some nature notes. Write down the different kinds of butterflies that visit your garden. Notice which flowers they go to the most. Maybe there's a butterfly you really wanted to see and didn't. Look at your butterfly books again. Find out what its favorite flower is. Next year, be sure to plant it.

1. What is the first step you should take to plant a butterfly garden?

2. What is nectar?

3. What should you do first: choose your flowers or find out the names of different flowers?

4. What colors do butterflies like?

5. What should you do if a butterfly you really wanted to see doesn't come to your garden?

Apply   **Directions** Read the following article. Then answer the questions that follow.

Cats, Big and Small
by Drew Moore

When you think of cats, you may think of the cats people have as pets. There are other kinds of cats, too. And some of them are not the kind you would want as a pet.

You could put all the different kinds of cats into three main groups. The first group is made up of large cats. The second group is made up of small cats. The bobcat is in this group. The third group is made up of house cats. These are the pets that people have. A Siamese is a house cat.

You probably know a little about one of the large cats. The lion is known as the king of beasts. It is a large wild cat. Lions have strong jaws and large, sharp teeth. They use their teeth for killing and eating animals such as zebras. The male lion has a thick mane of hair around his head and neck. Lions live in Africa.

Small cats are the second group. These cats are not as big as lions and tigers, but they are bigger than cats people have as pets. The bobcat is in the small cat group. Bobcats live in woods and mountains all over the United States and Canada. Like the lion, the bobcat hunts animals. But the bobcat hunts small animals, such as birds and rabbits. The bobcat gets its name from its bobtail. A bobtail is a short and stubby tail.

The last group is the house cats. Some house cats have long hair. Some have short hair. Most house cats spend much of their time sleeping. They curl up in chairs or on beds. They do not roar like lions. They meow. Like other cats, house cats can hunt. They especially like mice. House cats do not usually have to hunt, though. Their owners feed them every day.

1. What did the author write about in this article?

_____

_____

2. What are the three main groups of cats?

_____

_____

3. What animal is called the "king of the beasts"?

_____

_____

4. Where do bobcats live?

_____

_____

_____

5. Why wouldn't some cats make good pets?

_____

_____

_____

Assessment Practice   **Directions** Answer each question about the article you just read.

1 **Why did the author write this article?**

A   to explain how to take care of a cat

B   to tell about a Siamese cat

C   to tell information about different kinds of cats

D   to make you like cats

2 **Where do lions live?**

A   in the United States

B   in Canada

C   in houses as pets

D   in Africa

Focus on California Content Standards

Lesson 14 Ask Questions

Standard 2RC2.4 Ask clarifying questions about essential textual elements of exposition (e.g., *why, what if, how*).

When you read, it helps to ask yourself questions. It will help you understand what you read. The best way to start asking questions is to use the **5Ws and H** questions: Who? What? Where? When? Why? How? You may also want to ask yourself a "what if" question. It can help take your research many different ways.

When you ask questions, it can help you understand the information that you read. Think of something that you are interested in knowing more about. Fill in the blank lines after each question word. Use a separate sheet of paper if you need more room.

Who ---?

What --?

When --?

Where ---?

Why ---?

How ---?

What if ---?

Guided Reading Instruction

Directions Read the following article. Use the questions on the side to guide your reading.

California Sea Lions
by Emmy Clark

Guided Questions

1 California sea lions live up and down the coast of California. There are a lot of big rocks and sandy beaches. Sea lions like rocks and sandy beaches. They also like coves and tide pools. The also spend time swimming near big docks and jetties. Jetties are walls that have been built out into the sea to protect an area of land.

1 Where do California sea lions live

2 Sea lions have small heads. They have long narrow bodies. This makes them very good swimmers. The shape of their bodies helps them swim fast. This is good because they spend most of their time in the water. They can swim up to 18 miles an hour. They also have front flippers with nails. **3** They move their front flippers up and down. This helps them move fast through the water. It also helps them get away from sharks and killer whales. Sharks and killer whales are a big danger for sea lions. These creatures like to hunt the young pups. They are not the only problem for sea lions.

2 Why are sea lions good swimmers?

3 How do their front flippers help them?

Humans create problems too. Sometimes sea lions get caught in fishing nets. People dump garbage in the ocean. Garbage can make sea lions sick if they eat it. Sometimes ropes get caught around their necks. Sea lions also get plastic rings caught around their necks. These rings are from soda cans. Ropes and plastic rings can cut their skin. They can also stop them from eating. This is why it is important not to litter when you visit the beach. If you go out in a boat, never throw anything into the ocean.

Sea lions like to "talk" a lot. They bark like dogs. They click. They chirp, and they squeak. Each sea lion has its own sound. If a pup gets lost, its mother has a special wail. When the pup hears that wail, it cries back with its own special sound. This continues over and over again until the mother and pup find each other.

Sea lions are very playful. One of their favorite activities is to surf in front of waves. **4** Young sea lions also like to chase each other. Another activity pups like is to push each other off the rocks. They spend a lot of time on rocks. When they sit on the rocks, they like to point their noses up. They also like to lie on top of one another. This is often how they sleep. But one of their favorite ways to sleep is to float on their backs. Usually, all you can see is a nose and whiskers sticking up out of the water!

4 Read this sentence and the next. What do young sea lions like to do?

There are still a lot of sea lions today **5** It's important to make sure that the number of sea lions does not get smaller. Make sure that you do your part. Don't throw anything on the beach or in the ocean. Put it in a litter basket or a garbage bag.

5 What if the number of sea lions gets smaller? How can people help them?

1. When are sea lions in danger?

_____

_____

_____

2. How fast can sea lions swim?

_____

_____

3. Why is it important not to litter at the beach or in the ocean?

_____

_____

_____

_____

4. What is a favorite way that sea lions sleep?

_____

_____

_____

5. What if you were walking on the beach with a family member and you saw old plastic rings from soda cans? What would you do?

_____

_____

   Measuring Up® to the California Content Standards

Apply

Directions Read the following article. Then answer the questions.

Kids Make a Big Difference
by Molly Lowry

Across America, kids are making a big difference. Here's why! They are finding different ways to take care of the earth. Some kids are turning empty lots into beautiful gardens. Other kids are helping fish. They are asking people not to dump chemicals in streams. One young man started cleaning up rivers in his state. He walked many miles picking up litter. Now he has a big group of volunteers who help him.

We only have one earth! If people don't keep it clean, animals will die. Plants and flowers will die. The earth won't look pretty anymore. Here's what you can do to help!

Get together some family members. Find a place that has litter. Invite everyone to a cleanup day. Clean up the spot. Then make a plan to keep it clean.

Find a spot in your neighborhood that needs flowers or trees. Have a yard sale. Raise money. Buy flowers or a tree. Plant them.

Make sure you and your neighbors recycle. Draw posters. Put them up around your neighborhood. If they don't recycle, ask to them to recycle paper. Recycle cans. Recycle glass. Recycle plastic. Recycle everything they can.

Get together some friends. Find a place to volunteer. Maybe there is a place in your community that needs to be cleaned up. Perhaps there are park benches that you can paint. Maybe you can weed a garden. Ask what you can do in your community.

Get some classmates together. Design boxes and bags. Put the boxes and bags everywhere. Put them in your classrooms. Put them on your playground. Put them in the school lunchroom. Take time to remind students to recycle. Remember, sometimes it takes time for people to change. One way to help is to remind them to recycle. Remember to be friendly and nice.

Make a bulletin board at school. Show pictures of kids who care and what they do to keep the earth beautiful.

Make small booklets. Hand them out. Show people what they can do to keep their community free of litter.

You can make a difference. Across America, kids already have. So, if you care about the earth, take some time. Plant some flowers. Plant a tree. Clean a stream with a family member. Paint a bench. And remember, be kind to the earth every day. NEVER LITTER!

 Measuring Up® to the California Content Standards

Directions: What questions can you ask to help you understand the article? Write the question on the top line. Then read the article again. Find an answer to each question. Write each answer on the bottom line. Use a separate sheet of paper if you need more room.

1. Who?

2. What?

3. When?

4. Where?

5. Why?

_____

- -

_____

_____

- -

_____

6. How?

_____

- -

_____

_____

- -

_____

7. What if?

_____

- -

_____

_____

- -

_____

Assessment Practice

Directions Answer each question about the article you just read.

1 What is the most important step you can take to keep the earth clean?

A Recycle paper, cans, glass, and plastic.

B Throw paper napkins on the beach.

C Pick flowers in the park.

D Draw posters of animals.

2 What if people don't take care of the earth? Which of the following sentences BEST explains what might happen some day?

A Plants and animals might die because the earth is not clean.

B There will be a lot more trees.

C There will be a lot more animals and birds.

D There will be more flowers and plants.

Focus on California Content Standards

Lesson 15   Restate Facts and Details

Standard 2RC2.4 Restate facts and details in the text to organize and clarify ideas.

Facts are pieces of information that are true. Facts can be many different things, such as names of people or places, dates, how big things are, or how much things weigh. You can check facts to make sure they are true. The information can be found in articles and books. Here is a fact: The San Diego Zoo opens every day at 9 A.M.

Details give more information. Details can give information about people and places. Details can tell how to make or do something, how something works. They can also tell how something looks, smells, tastes, sounds, or feels. Here is a detail: You can see elephants playing on the zoo's "Elephant Cam."

Guided Reading Instruction

Directions Read the following article. Use the questions on the side to guide your reading.

Thank You Mr. Binney and Mr. Smith!
by Djeema Jensen

1 Crayons were made a long time ago. You might think they were made in the United States first. They weren't. The first crayons were made in Europe. They were made of charcoal and oil.

Later on, powdered colors replaced the charcoal. The oil was changed to wax **2** The wax made the crayons much easier to use. It also made the crayons stronger. These crayons were shipped to schools in America. It cost a lot of money to ship them. It also took a long time because the crayons were shipped by boat. Two people in America got to thinking. **3** Joseph W. Binney and C. Harold Smith were cousins. In 1885, they formed a company. It was called Binney & Smith. It was located in a town in New York State.

In 1900, the two men bought an old factory in Pennsylvania. It was near a place where there were a lot of rocks. Binney and Smith needed this kind of rock to make pencils. The rock is called slate. It is a hard gray rock. This kind of rock makes pencils. They sold the pencils to schools and got to know the teachers.

Teachers began to ask them for better chalk. They said the chalk was too dusty. It fell apart. Binney & Smith invented a new chalk. The teachers liked it.

The teachers also asked for crayons. The crayons from Europe were very good, but they cost too much money. Binney and Smith already made wax crayons. They were used to mark crates and barrels. But some of the colors were unsafe. They weren't good for children.

Guided Questions

1 Read the first paragraph. Underline the fact that tells where crayons were made first.

2 Why did wax replace oil?

3 Read this paragraph. Underline the names of the two people who started a company. Where was the company located?

Binney and Smith asked people at their company to find safe colors. Workers in the lab studied powdered colors for a long time. Finally, they found a way to make the colors safe.

4 In 1903, their first box of crayons was made. There were eight crayons. The crayons were packed in a box. The colors were purple, orange, yellow, blue, green, black, brown, and red. The box sold for 5 cents. This price was much less than the crayons from Europe.

4 In your own words, explain what happened in 1903.

Through the years, Binney and Smith added more crayon colors. In 2003, four new colors were added. Two of the colors were mango tango and jazzberry jam. Today, there are 120 different colors. And there are new names! There have been other additions. There are crayons that glitter in the dark. There are crayons that smell like flowers. Some crayons change colors. Other crayons wash off walls.

5 Here's one more piece of information! In 2001, a poll was taken. People were asked what color they liked best. It was blue—just plain blue! Not inch worm! Not cotton candy! Not macaroni and cheese. Just plain blue!

5 Read this paragraph. Underline an important detail.

1. Read these sentences.

> Binney and Smith already made wax crayons. Their crayons were used to mark crates and barrels. But some of the colors were unsafe. They weren't good for children.

What details tell how their crayons were used? Circle them.

_____

- -
_____

- -
_____

2. Read these sentences.

> Binney and Smith needed this kind of rock to make pencils. The rock is called slate. It is a hard gray rock. This kind of rock makes very good pencils. They sold the pencils to schools and got to know the teachers.

Underline the details that tell why Binney and Smith needed this kind of rock. Then write a sentence of your own that tells about this rock.

_____

- -
_____

- -
_____

- -
_____

Apply   **Directions** Read this article. Then answer the questions that follow.

A Great Little Pet
by Lucy Clark Owens

Some kids have cats, and some kids have dogs. Some kids have hamsters, and some kids have fish. But my vote for a cute pet is a hermit crab. Did you ever think about getting one? Well, you shouldn't get just one. You really should get two or three. They like company.

Crabs travel in big groups in the wild. There might up to 100 crabs in a group. This way they can make more shell changes. It works like this. One crab finds a new shell and moves into it. Another crab changes into that crab's old shell. Then another crab changes shells and another and another!

Hermit crabs are very cute, and they are fun! They also make chirping noises. They don't exactly sound like birds. They don't sound like frogs. They sound a little bit like a bird and a little bit like a frog. And a little bit like a creaking door! Well, it's a sound that is hard to describe. But it's fun to hear.

There are about 500 different kinds of hermit crabs. They live all over the world. Some hermit crabs live on the ocean floor. Some live on land.

Hermit crabs do not have a hard shell. They live in shells they find. As they grow bigger, they must find new shells. The shell must be hard so it can protect them. They find old shells that belonged to other animals.

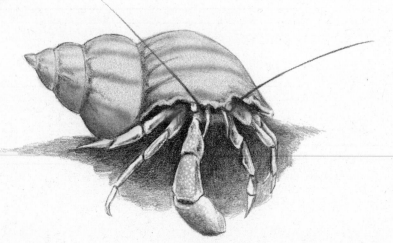

Hermit crabs are different colors. They can be red, brown, or purple. Some hermit crabs have stripes. Some have dots. They have 10 legs. Two of the legs are in the front of the crab. These two legs have big claws on them. The claws are used to pick up food. These claws are also used to pinch so be careful if you pick one up!

Hermit crabs eat many different kinds of food. In the ocean, they live on plants and animals. As pets, they like to eat everything! They like apples and grapes. They like vegetables. They even like meatballs! They aren't fussy.

If you decide to get a few hermit crabs, make sure you make them a nice little house. You can use an aquarium. Make sure it's roomy. Have a place for food and water. Hermit crabs like to climb and play. Use parts of tree branches, or use a tiny ladder so they can climb and have fun. You might also want to put in small flowerpots. But make sure they are unpainted. These crabs like to hide! Make a little pool so they can swim. Also, be sure to leave room for them to walk around.

Buy sand for the bottom of their home. Hermit crabs like to walk and run in sand. You can buy playground sand at a hardware store. It costs about $2.50 for 25 pounds.

Finally, don't forget some pretty shells in different sizes. When it's time for a bigger shell, you want your pet to have a choice! If you take care of your hermit crabs, they can live for quite awhile. Have fun!

1. Read these sentences.

> Crabs travel in big groups in the wild. There might be up to 100 crabs in a group. This way they can make more shell changes. It works like this. One crab finds a new shell and moves into it. Another crab changes into that crab's old shell. Then another crab changes shells and another and another!

Underline the fact that tells how many crabs there can be in a group. How do crabs find new shells?

_____

_____

_____

_____

2. Explain why hermit crabs are fun pets. Remember to use details.

_____

_____

_____

_____

3. About how many different kinds of hermit crabs are there?

_____

_____

4. What kinds of foods can you feed a pet hermit crab? Use two details in your answer.

_____

_____

_____

_____

5. For what do hermit crabs use their front claws?

_____

_____

_____

_____

Assessment Practice   **Directions** Answer each question about the article you just read.

1 **Which of the following is true about hermit crabs?**

A They don't like to eat anything but plants.

B As they grow bigger, they have to find a new shell.

C They don't like to play.

D They hide in the sand and never come out.

2 **Which of the following statements is NOT true about hermit crabs?**

A They eat many kinds of food.

B They like to live alone and don't like company.

C They can have dots and stripes.

D They can be red, brown, or purple.

Focus on California Content Standards

| Lesson 16 | Identify Cause and Effect |

Standard 2RC2.6 Recognize cause-and-effect relationships in a text.

A **cause** is why something happens. An **effect** is what it's like afterwards.

As you read, ask yourself these questions:

<u>What happened?</u> and <u>What happened afterwards?</u>

Cause	Effect
 The chicken got hit with an acorn.	 She was scared that the sky was falling.
 Pedro and Dan were fishing and a skunk came by.	 They ran away.

The word **because** is important. It tells you to look for a cause and effect. For example,

The chicken was scared that the sky was falling **because** she got hit with an acorn.

Pedro and Dan ran away **because** a skunk came by.

Guided Reading Instruction

Directions Read the following article. Use the questions on the side to guide your reading. Then answer the questions that follow.

Keep the Forest Safe
by Christy Gilbert

A forest is an amazing place. It has a lot of trees. It has a lot of plants. **1** Many animals and birds live in forests because there are a lot of trees. The trees give them food and places to live.

Guided Questions

1 Underline why animals live in forests.

People also depend on forests. Here are some things people get from trees. We get maple syrup. People put maple syrup on their pancakes. We get cocoa beans. People use these beans to make chocolate. We get nuts. People use nuts to make brownies. We get wood. People use wood to make paper. People also use wood to build houses and make pencils.

Forests cover a lot of land on the earth. This is very important because the trees give living things oxygen. Oxygen is a gas. It is what people and animals breath to stay alive. Forests also help to control the temperature of the earth. The land would get too hot if there weren't any forests. **2** Many animals would die because they would not have places to live. They would not be able to find food.

Protect the Forests

It is very important to protect our forests. If you go camping, never play with matches. If you see other children playing with matches, tell a grownup right away. If grown-ups make a campfire, help them find rocks. Use the rocks to make a circle around the campfire. Help grown-ups watch the campfire. Never walk away from the fire. Fire sparks might fly. You want to see them if that happens. **3** A spark might cause a tree or bush to catch on fire. Make sure there is a bucket of water and shovel near the fire. A bucket and shovel are very important because they can help you put out a fire.

Now you can enjoy yourself because your campfire is safe. Roast marshmallows. Tell scary stories. Wait for the flames to get very low. Then listen to the night sounds! Before you go to bed, make sure an older family member has put out the fire.

Forest Fires

Sometimes the weather is hot. Sometimes it is dry. Sometimes it is windy. Sometimes is it hot, dry, and windy at the same time. This is not good. When this happens, there is the danger of a fire. **4** A fire in a forest is very dangerous because it can burn down all the trees. It can hurt animals. It can hurt people. Fires can be started by bolts of lightning that hit trees. The trees catch fire. Very often, careless people start forest fires.

Guided Questions

2 What would happen if there weren't any forests? What do the trees give the animals?

3 What can happen if you walk away from a campfire?

4 Name two effects of forest fires.

Fire Fighters

If there is a forest fire, there are special fire fighters. These people know how to fight big fires. They wear big boots to protect their feet. They wear gloves to protect their hands. They wear clothes that are treated with special chemicals so they won't burn easily. **5** They cover their faces with masks to protect them from flames and smoke. It's tough work. Fire fighters are very brave and fearless.

Guided Questions

5 Why do fire fighters wear masks?

1. The picture below shows an effect. Draw a picture that shows the cause. Then write a sentence to state the cause and effect.

Cause	**Effect**
	It was so warm, the snowman started to melt.

2. The picture shows a cause. Draw a picture that shows the effect. Then write a sentence to state the cause and effect.

Cause   **Effect**

The mother duck told her ducklings to watch how she flies.

Apply **Directions** Read the article below. Then answer the questions that follow.

Gold in the River
by Lily Yellowbird

One day a long time ago, a man was chopping wood. He was near a river. His name was James Marshall. Marshall saw a gold nugget. The nugget was in the river. Marshall said, "The piece was about half the size and shape of a pea. Then I saw another."

Marshall worked for John Sutter. Sutter had moved to California in 1839. He wanted to build a huge farming kingdom. He built a big fort. He planted a lot of crops and bought many cattle. He was very successful.

In 1847, Sutter sent James Marshall and other workers to build a sawmill. A sawmill is a place where people cut logs into lumber. They built the sawmill next to a river because they moved the logs along the river to different places.

Marshall told him about the gold. Sutter made Marshall and the others promise they wouldn't tell anyone. Sutter wanted to build his kingdom. He didn't want to look for gold. It took only a few months before the secret was out. The rush for gold began.

Soon, Sutter's workmen left him to search for gold. People started to camp on his land because it was near the river. They ruined the land. They killed his animals. They trampled his crops. By 1852, Sutter was broke. He had nothing left.

Other people made a lot of money though. Sam Brannan heard about the gold. He lived in San Francisco. He wanted to get rich too! This is what he did! He ran through the streets. He held a little bottle over his head. He said it was gold dust. People listened. Word spread. Soon many people moved west because they wanted to get rich.

Brannan got rich very fast. He bought shovels and metal pans. He bought axes. He sold them to miners. He made a lot of money in just nine weeks!

It was 1849. People had big dreams. It was a world event. People came from Mexico. They came from China. Men traveled west. Women traveled west. Not everyone looked for gold. There were other ways to make money because the miners needed food, clothes and a safe place to keep their gold.

Chicken farmers sold eggs. One woman made pies. She sold them to the miners. They ate the pies for lunch. Another woman sold flour. Some women panned for gold.

One man made overalls because the miners needed sturdy pants. His name was Levi Strauss. One day a miner walked into his shop. He said that his pants kept falling apart. The cloth was not strong enough. The cloth tore when he bent over or kneeled to pan for gold. Strauss found a strong fabric to make pants. The miners liked the pants, but the cloth was too rough. The cloth rubbed against their skin and made it sore. Finally, Strauss found another cloth. It was strong, and the miners liked it.

Henry Wells and William Fargo started a bank. There were robberies in the mining camps. Miners couldn't find safe places to hide their gold or money. The bank was a safe place. Wells and Fargo also started a mail service because people wanted to get mail from home.

People made a lot of money, but it didn't last. People were still moving west because they wanted to find gold. But the gold was getting harder to find. Many of the miners gave up their dreams. They returned home. Others stayed. They just had to find gold. Sometimes they did, but it wasn't very often.

San Francisco got bigger and bigger. It had been very small. The gold rush changed everything. New houses were built. Newspapers were started. People wanted opera. They wanted theater. San Franciso became a great city. It was because of one man. He saw something sparkle. He picked it up! It was a tiny piece of gold!

1. Why did Sutter move to California?

_____

_____

_____

_____

2. Why did Sutter's men leave him?

_____

_____

3. Why did the miners need a safe place for their gold and money?

_____

_____

_____

_____

4. Read this sentence.

> They built the sawmill near a river because they moved the logs along the river to different places.

Underline why the sawmill was near a river.

_____

- -

_____

_____

- -

_____

5. What happened to San Francisco as a result of all those people moving west?

_____

- -

_____

Assessment Practice   **Directions** Answer each question about the article you just read.

1 **What happened because so many people camped on Sutter's land?**

A He made a lot of money.

B His land was ruined.

C He grew more crops

D He was given a lot of gold.

2 **What is the reason Strauss made overalls?**

A He liked overalls.

B He needed something to sell.

C Miners needed sturdy pants.

D Farmers needed overalls.

Focus on California Content Standards

Lesson 17 Read Charts, Graphs, and Diagrams

Standard 2RC2.7 Interpret information from diagrams, charts, and graphs.

Sometimes writers show information in a diagram, chart, or graph.

A **diagram** is a drawing or a picture that shows how to do or make something. It can also show how something looks. A diagram can show how to put together an airplane. It can show the different parts of a frog.

A **chart** is a group of facts that are all about one topic. A chart might show different facts about grasshoppers.

A **graph** displays **data,** or numbers, in a chart form. The data can be shown in different kinds of graphs. It might be a picture graph or a bar graph. A graph might show how many people rode on the roller coaster during one week.

Guided Reading Instruction

Directions Read the following article. Use the questions on the side to guide your reading. Then answer the questions that follow.

Follow That Ant
by James Ogle

Guided Questions

Have you ever watched an ant crawling along outside? Did you know what it was doing or where it was going? The ant you saw was a worker ant. It was looking for food or taking food back to its home.

You have probably seen part of an ant's home, too. You may have seen the little mound of dirt surrounding a hole. This is the entrance to the ant's home, which is called an anthill. Most of the anthill is under the ground. There is one main tunnel. There are many small parts, or rooms, off the tunnels. The worker ants dig the rooms and the tunnels of an anthill.

Diagram 1

Queen

Soldier Ants

1

Worker
Ants

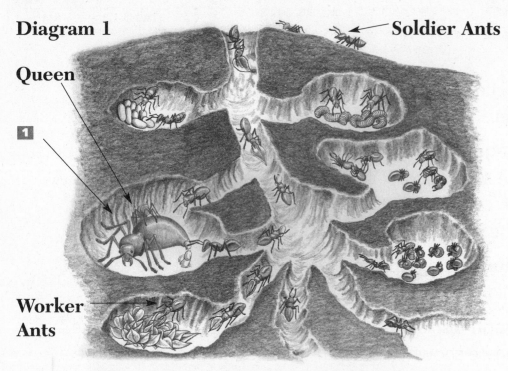

This is what an an anthill looks like. 2

Different kinds of ants live in an anthill. Most of the ants
are worker ants. These ants make the anthill, and they look
for food. They also take out the garbage. Ants are very neat.
They don't like garbage! All worker ants are females. The
most important female ant is called the queen. The queen
spends her whole life laying eggs, which become baby ants.
That's all she does. Worker ants feed her and take care of her.
Worker ants also feed and do other things for baby ants.

Diagram 2

Eye

Head

Pincher

3 Claw

Feeler

Front Leg

Middle Leg

Rear Leg

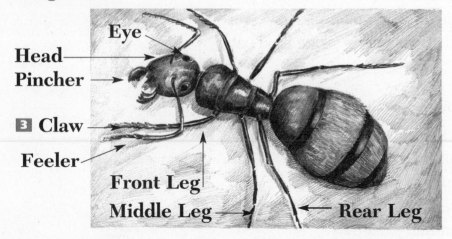

This shows the parts of an ant's body.

1 What do you notice
about the queen?
What does the
queen do?

2 What does the
diagram show?

3 Look at the diagram
of an ant's body.
What is at the end
of each front leg?
How do you think
ants use their claws?

 Measuring Up® to the California Content Standards

There are other ants called soldiers. These ants protect the entrance of the anthill. They also travel with and protect the worker ants as they look for food.

Just what kinds of food do the worker ants look for? Ants eat a lot of things. They eat dead bugs. They also eat leaves and other food they find outside. You may have seen ants crawling around a picnic table. Can you guess what they were doing?

---

4 Ant Fact Sheet
- An ant lives between 45–60 days.
- An ant has feelers. The feelers help them smell and taste.
- An ant has two stomachs. One stomach holds its own food.
- The other stomach holds food to share with other ants.
- Ants are different colors. Some ants are black. Some are red. They can also be yellow, purple, brown, or green. **5**

---

4 What does the writer use to show the ant facts?

5 Which ant fact do you think is most interesting? Explain why.

1. Look at Diagram 1. How many ants are protecting the anthill?

   _____

   -

   _____

2. Look at Diagram 1. What are the ants carrying down the tunnel? Where are they taking them?

   _____

   -

   _____

3. Look at Diagram 2. What does an ant have at the top of its head? What do you think these do?

   _____

   -

   _____

   -

   _____

4. Look at the chart. How many stomachs does an ant have? Which fact gives you this information?

   _____

   -

   _____

5. Look at the chart. What colors can ants be? Which fact gives you this information?

   _____

   -

   _____

   -

   _____

Measuring Up® to the California Content Standards

Apply   **Directions** Read the article below. Then answer the questions that follow.

Pond Life
by Emmy Clark

Isabella is giving a report at school in two weeks. It is about pond life. Every Saturday, she and her mom walk over to Painted Turtle Pond. It's spring. There is a lot going on. There are ducks and ducklings. There are tadpoles. There's lot of peeping. There's a lot of buzzing. There's a lot to hear and see.

Every time they visit, Isabella sees something new. Last week, she saw tadpoles. She asked her mom about them. Her mom told her that tadpoles are part of the life cycle of a frog. The tadpoles had just hatched from frog eggs. Her mom drew this picture.

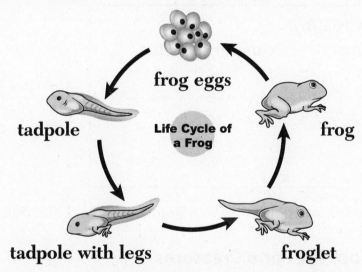

Isabella is very interested in frogs. She would like to have a pet frog. She likes the sounds they make. She also likes to watch them jump. But her mom says it is better to leave frogs in ponds. She thinks the tadpoles are funny. They are born with tails, but they lose them as they get older. Tadpoles use their tails to swim. Sometimes she wonders if they miss their tails when they disappear. This idea makes her laugh.

Isabella also likes spring peepers. They make a lot of noise but only in spring. Spring peepers are little frogs. They live in trees around ponds. They really peep a lot. No matter how hard Isabella looks she can never see them. But she likes to hear them at night when she goes to sleep.

There is another creature Isabella really likes to see at the pond. It is called a water strider. It is also called a pond skater. Isabella likes the name pond skater better. She pretends that it wears skates to walk on water. That's what it does. It walks on water. It's very fast. It hardly ever goes under the water.

After several weeks of looking, Isabella writes her report. She puts together her pictures of pond life. She wants her classmates to see pond life up close.

Isabella gives her report. Her classmates really like it. After the report, Isabella takes a survey. She asks her classmates this question:

Which pond creature would you like to see most? She writes their answers on a chart. It looks like this.

Top Five Pond Creatures

Name of Creature	Number of Votes
1. Turtle	4
2. Crayfish	2
3. Pond Skater	10
4. Tree Peeper	6
5. Tadpole	8

Then she used the information to make a graph. It looked like this.

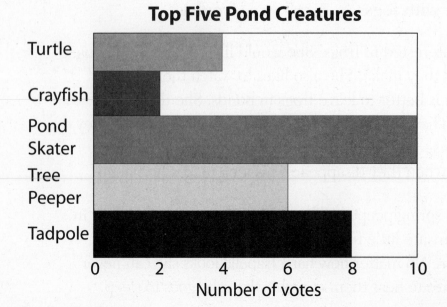

Top Five Pond Creatures

1. Look at the diagram of a frog's life cycle. When the eggs hatch, what do they become?

_____

- -

_____

2. Look at the graph. What does the graph show?

_____

- -

_____

3. What does Isabella do after her report? Which creature would the children like to see most? How many votes did the pond skater get?

_____

- -

_____

_____

- -

_____

Assessment Practice   **Directions** Answer each question about the article you just read.

1 Based on the diagram of the frog, what is the next thing to grow on a tadpole?

A tongue

B hands

C tail

D legs

2 How many fewer votes did the tree peeper get than the tadpole?

A 4

B 3

C 2

D 1

Instructions are directions that tell you how to do something. It is important to know how to follow them.

Instructions start out by listing what you need. This list shows what you need to make blueberry pancakes!

What You Will Need

1 cup flour
2 teaspoons baking powder
1/2 teaspoon salt
1/4 teaspoon vanilla
1 egg
1/2 cup milk
1 cup blueberries

Steps come after the list of what you will need. The steps tell you how to do something. They are always in order. Look at these steps. They show you how to make pancakes.

Step1: Measure flour and put in bowl.
Step 2: Add baking powder. Then mix.
Step 3: Add salt to bowl. Then mix.
Step 4: Add egg and mix.
Step 5: Add milk and vanilla. Then mix.
Step 6: Mix in 1 cup of blueberries.

Sometimes there are two parts in a step. For example, look at step 2. First, you add the baking powder. Then you mix.

When you read instructions, remember to do every step in the order it is given.

Guided Reading Instruction

Directions Read the following instructions. Use the questions on the side to guide your reading. Then answer the questions that follow.

Khcaf: A Sweet Drink from Algeria, North Africa

Guided Questions

1 Khchaf is a fruit drink. It is from Algeria. Algeria is a country. It is in North Africa. Sometimes it is very hot there. People like to drink cold drinks. Cold drinks cool them down on very hot days. This is one of the drinks people like to drink.

1 Underline what khchaf is.

Khchaf

2 A Sweet Drink from Algeria, North Africa

2 From what country is this drink? Where is this country?

3 WHAT YOU'LL NEED

2 quarts water
2 sticks cinnamon
1/2 cup raisins
sugar, to taste
4 medium-sized saucepan
mixing spoon

3 Underline the ingredients you need to make this drink.

4 What size saucepan do you need?

*WHAT TO DO

1. Bring water with cinnamon sticks to boil in saucepan.
2. Add raisins, reduce heat, and simmer for 15 minutes.
3. Stir in sugar.
4. Remove from heat and take out cinnamon sticks.
5. Allow liquid to cool for one hour, then refrigerate for 45 minutes.
6. Pour into glasses, adding a few raisins to each glass. **5**

5 What should you do after you pour the fruit drink into a glass?

*IMPORTANT: Make sure an older family member is with you when you make this fruit drink. NEVER turn on the stove without an adult present.

1. Why do people like to drink this fruit drink?

- -

2. How many steps are there for this recipe?

- -

3. Which step tells you to add sugar? How much sugar should you add? Why?

- -

- -

4. What are the two parts of step 4?

- -

- -

5. What are the two parts of step 5?

- -

- -

Apply

Directions Read the instructions below. Then answer the questions that follow.

Let It Snow!
by Lily Yellowbird

Have you ever seen a snowflake? Well, maybe you have or maybe you haven't. It depends on where you live. A snowflake is like a little piece of magic. No two snowflakes have the same design. Every snowflake is different.

What You Will Need

- square sheets of paper in different colors
- pencil
- a pair of scissors*

What to Do

Step 1: Draw a line to make two triangles on a square piece of paper. Then fold in half.	
Step 2: Write A, B, C, and D. Fold corner A to corner B.	
Step 3: Now the triangle shows corners D, C, and AB. Fold corner AB to corner C.	

* Be very careful when you use your scissors.

What to Do

Step 4: Draw lines where you want to cut.	D
Step 5: Use your scissors. Cut out a snowflake design. NOTE: Remember D is the center of your snowflake. It should be at the top. If you are right-handed, the fold should be on your right. If you are left-handed, the fold should be on your left.	D ——— center of snowflake
Step 6: Open your snowflake. If you want to change your design, fold up the snowflake and make more cuts.	

Hang the snowflakes around your classroom. Have a snowflake party.

1. Which step tells you to draw a line to make two triangles?

- -

_____

2. What are the two parts in Step 2?

- -

_____

- -

_____

- -

3. Where is D located on the diagram in step 2?

- -

_____

4. Which step tells you to fold corner C to corner AB?

- -

_____

5. Which letter shows you the center of your snowflake?

- -

_____

Assessment Practice

Directions Answer each question based on the instructions you just read.

1 **Which step tells you to cut out a snowflake design?**

A Step 3

B Step 4

C Step 5

D Step 6

2 **If you want to change your design, which step should you do again?**

A Fold up the snowflake, and make more cuts.

B Keep your snowflake open, and make more cuts.

C Fold in different places, and more cuts.

D Make a new snowflake.

 Measuring Up® to the California Content Standards

Read this selection. Then answer the questions that follow it.

Ice Cream Stories
by Gabriella Gomez

Do you know who Augustus Jackson is? Probably not, but you might want to know. He is called "the father of ice cream."

Jackson was an African American man. He was a chef at the White House. He decided to leave. He wanted to start his own company. He moved to Philadelphia, Pennsylvania. It was in the 1820s.

When he got there, he started his own food company. He started to make ice cream. He made very big batches! People had not made batches before. It was hard to keep them cold. Jackson found a way. He mixed ice and salt into the recipe. This kept the ice cream cold. He put the ice cream in tin cans. Then he took the cans around the city.

Jackson worked hard. He sold a lot of ice cream to people. He also sold ice cream to two ice cream shops. The shops were on South Street. Two African American men owned these shops.

Jackson made a lot of money, and he became very rich. His business lasted for about 30 years.

There were other African American people who made ice cream in this city. Augustus Jackson was the most famous. People really liked his flavors. Two popular flavors were vanilla and lemon. Later on, other people became famous for their ice cream, too.

In 1854, William Breyer started to make ice cream. He made ice cream in his own kitchen. He used the freshest cream and milk. Then he rode around on his wagon. He sold the ice cream on the street. Later on, he opened six shops where he sold ice cream. He became very famous. He died in 1882. His sons took over the business.

In 1861, Louis Dubois Bassett started to make ice cream. He made it at home. By 1885, he sold ice cream all over the city. He worked hard for many, many years. He finally opened his own shop. It was 1893. The shop is still there! The Bassett family still owns it!

Ice cream became very popular. There is one big reason. Everything in it was fresh. It was made with fresh cream and milk. It didn't use any eggs. A lot of ice cream was made with eggs. But not in Philadelphia! It hasn't changed! Only these ingredients are still used:

- cream
- milk
- sugar
- flavorings

At one time, Philadelphia was called the ice cream capital of our country. All that has changed! Ice cream is made by a lot of people now. It is sold everywhere. It is sold on the street. It is sold at the store. It is sold at baseball games. It is sold at the zoo. It is a very BIG business. People like many different flavors.

This chart shows the top four! Is one of these your favorite? Or, do you have another flavor you like?

Top Four Ice Cream Flavors
1. vanilla
2. chocolate
3. butter pecan
4. strawberry

So, the next time you have ice cream, remember Augustus Jackson. Have a big scoop just for him!

   Measuring Up® to the California Content Standards

1 The author uses the FIRST TWO paragraphs

A to explain how to make ice cream.

B to tell about favorite flavors of ice cream.

C to tell about Augustus Jackson.

D to tell the top four flavors.

This is part of a book's table of contents. Use it to answer questions 2 and 3.

2 If you are reading page 9, which chapter are you reading?

A Chapter 1

B Chapter 2

C Chapter 3

D Chapter 4

3 In which chapter would you find information about different flavors?

A Chapter 1

B Chapter 2

C Chapter 3

D Chapter 4

4 Why did Augustus Jackson become a rich man?

A He was a very good chef.

B He sold a lot of ice cream.

C He sold small batches of ice cream.

D He had many ice cream shops.

5 Which of the following statements about William Breyer is true?

A Breyer started to make ice cream in 1854.

B Breyer sold his ice cream from a horse.

C Breyer opened only two shops.

D His sons sold the business when he died.

6 What did Augustus Jackson do that other ice cream makers had not done?

A He didn't use ice and salt.

B He used ice and salt to make large batches.

C He made interesting flavors.

D He hired other people to make the ice cream.

7 Which of these is NOT used to make ice cream?

A cream

B milk

C sugar

D bread

8 What effect did mixing ice and salt into the ice cream recipe have?

A It made the ice cream melt.

B It made the ice cream taste good.

C It made the ice cream cold.

D It made the ice cream smooth.

9 Look at this chart.

> *Top Four Ice Cream Flavors*
> 1. vanilla
> 2. chocolate
> 3. butter pecan
> 4. strawberry

Which ice cream is the MOST popular flavor?

A vanilla

B chocolate

C butter pecan

D strawberry

10 Which of the following people did NOT make ice cream in the 1800s?

A Augustus Jackson

B William Breyer

C Jerry Greenfield

D Louis Dubois Bassett

Lesson 19   Understand Plot

Focus on California Content Standards

Standard 2RC3.1   Compare and contrast plots, settings and character presented by different authors

Standard 2RC3.2   Generate alternative endings to plots and identify the reason or reasons for, and the impact of, the alternatives.

The **plot** is a plan for a story. It is what happens to the main character. The main character usually faces a problem. The problem has to be solved. The story ends when the main character solves the problem.

When you read, pay attention to the events. Ask yourself questions. What happens first? What happens next? What happens last? This can help you understand the plot.

It is also important to look for cause and effect. As you read, ask yourself these questions. What has happened? Why has it happened? These questions can help you figure out why something happened.

Think about how the story ends. Could it have ended in a different way? Think about other stories you have read. How are the plots alike? How are they different?

Guided Reading Instruction

Directions Read the following story. Use the questions on the side to guide your reading. Then, answer the questions that follow.

The Rooster and the Fox

based on a fable by Aesop
retold by Madeline Juran

Guided Questions

One evening Rooster flew up into a tree to sleep. He fluffed his feathers and flapped his wings three times.

But just before he tucked his head under his wing, Rooster spotted a flash of red. It was moving behind the barn. He looked again and saw Fox standing beneath the tree.

1 "Good evening, Rooster," said Fox. "Have you heard the good news?"

2 Rooster was afraid of Fox, but he tried not to show it. "News?" he asked calmly. "What news?"

3 "Why, all the animals have agreed to love one another," said Fox.

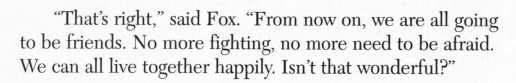

"Oh, really?" said Rooster, trying to sound pleasant.

"That's right," said Fox. "From now on, we are all going to be friends. No more fighting, no more need to be afraid. We can all live together happily. Isn't that wonderful?"

"Hmmm. That is great news, Fox."

4 "Yes, so why don't you come down from that tree so I can give you a great big hug?"

But Rooster did not come down. Instead, he stretched up on his tiptoes. He seemed to be looking at something far away.

"What are you looking at, Rooster?" asked Fox.

5 "I see the farmer's two dogs coming this way in a hurry," said Rooster.

"Maybe they want to tell us—"

"Did you say dogs?" cried Fox. "So long, Rooster. I forgot—I have some important errands to take care of." And he turned to run away.

"Wait!" cried Rooster. "Where are you going? The dogs are our friends now. Don't you want to give them a big hug, too?"

6 "No, thanks," Fox called back. "Maybe they haven't heard the good news yet." And off he ran across the pasture without a glance behind him.

6 What does Fox think will happen if he stays?

Rooster chuckled. "A big hug indeed!" he said to himself. "I wouldn't trust Fox as far as I could throw the farmer's tractor." Then he tucked his head under his wing and went to sleep.

1. Read the sentences below. Then, write 1, 2, 3, 4 to show the order of events.

_____ Rooster tucks his head under his wing and goes to sleep.

_____ Fox tells Rooster there is good news.

_____ Rooster sees Fox running behind the barn.

_____ Fox says that he has important errands and runs away.

2. How does Rooster solve his problem?

_____

- -

_____

- -

_____

Apply

Directions Read the story below. Then, answer the questions that follow.

Skunk Uses Her Head
by Diana C. Conway

Everybody had friends except Skunk. "I'll make someone be my friend," she said.

She found Possum sitting in a pine tree. Skunk lifted her black-and-white tail and said, "Be my friend or I'll spray you!"

Possum closed his eyes and pretended to sleep until Skunk went away.

Next, Skunk saw Raccoon washing her face in the pond. Skunk lifted her tail and said, "Play with me or I'll spray you!"

Raccoon put her head under the water and waited until Skunk went away.

Then Skunk spied Rabbit nibbling flowers in a grassy meadow. Skunk lifted her tail and said. "Say you like me or I'll spray you!"

Rabbit hopped away as fast as he could.

Sadly, Skunk sat down to rest in a rocky field. One rock got up and moved away from her.

"I see you, Turtle," called Skunk. "Stay with me or I''ll spray you!"

Turtle tucked her head and feet into her shell. "You'll never make friends that way," she said.

"How *can* I make friends?" asked Skunk

Deep in her shell Turtle whispered, "Use your head, not your tail."

 Measuring Up® to the California Content Standards

Use my head? What does Turtle mean? Skunk wondered. She hid behind a rock and watched Rabbit hop into the field. Rabbit put his soft nose down to Turtle's shell. Out popped Turtle's head. The two friends nuzzled noses in the moonlight. Skunk wanted to nuzzle noses, too, but she was afraid they would say no.

Skunk sighed and started back home. At the pond, she heard splashes. She watched Raccoon wash a water-lily root and share it with Flying Squirrel. Skunk wanted a bite of water-lily root, too, but she was afraid they would say no. She walked on alone.

At the pine tree, Skunk heard giggles. She watched the three Mouse sisters ask Possum to give them a ride on his back. "Glad to," said Possum. Skunk wanted to give the three Mouse sisters a ride on her back, too, but she was afraid they would say no. She walked on alone.

Skunk stopped to wipe her eyes with her tail. She seemed to be the only one in the forest without a friend. No, wait! Somebody else was walking alone in the moonlight. Porcupine waddled up to Skunk. He lifted his tail and rattled his sharp quills.

"Be my friend or I'll stick you with my quills," he said.

"You'll never make friends that way," said Skunk.

"How *can* I make friends?" asked Porcupine.

"Turtle told me to use my head, not my tail. Let's see. . . . Rabbit nuzzles noses, Raccoon shares lily roots, and Possum plays games."

Porcupine lowered his prickly tail. "I like games," he said. "What do you want to play?"

Skunk lowered her tail and said, "You can pick the game."

Porcupine and Skunk played hide-and-seek in the moonlight. One by one, the other animals came to watch.

"Two is OK for hide-and-seek," said Porcupine. "but more is better, don't you think?"

Skunk agreed. Skunk and Porcupine asked the others to join the game, and they all said yes. Even Turtle played. She always hid in her own shell.

1. Who is the main character?

- -

2. Who is the main character?

- -

3. Read the sentences below. Then, write 1, 2, 3, 4, 5 to show the order of events.

_____ Skunk watches Possum give the three Mouse sisters a ride.

_____ Turtle tells Skunk how to make friends.

_____ Skunk watches Raccoon share a water-lily root with Flying Squirrel.

_____ Skunk watches Turtle and Rabbit nuzzle noses.

_____ Porcupine and Skunk meet in the forest.

4. How do Skunk and Porcupine become friends?

- -

5. What happens at the end of the story?

_____

- -

_____

- -

_____

Assessment Practice   **Directions** Answer each question about the stories you just read.

1 **If Rooster had not used his head, how would the end of "The Rooster and the Fox" probably be different?**

A Rooster would have had Fox for dinner.

B Rooster and Fox would become friends.

C Fox would eat Rooster.

D D Rooster would stay up in the tree.

2 **How does Skunk use her head?**

A She figures out how to make friends with Porcupine.

B She learns how to play hide-and-seek.

C She washes a water-lily root and eats it.

D She nuzzles noses with Rabbit.

Focus on California Content Standards

Lesson 20   **Understand Characters**

Standard 2RL3.1   Compare and contrast plots, settings, and characters presented by different authors.

A **character** can be a person. A character can be an animal. The animal might act like a person.

Characters have different **traits.** Traits are qualities. For example, a character might be funny. A character might be smart. A character might be messy. A character might be sad.

You can tell what a character is like from what the character does and says. A character may say mean things. A character might act in a friendly way. A character may act silly all the time. A character can change in a story. A character may change from being mean to being very nice.

Pictures can tell about the characters. They help you see what a character is like. They can help you learn more about the character. Look at the picture below. You can tell what each character is like without even reading a story about them.

As you read, think about the characters. What do they say? What do they do? Are the characters like people in your life? Do they act as you would if you were in their place? Do they change? Or, do they stay the same?

Think about other characters in stories you have read. How are they alike? How are they different?

Guided Reading Instruction

Directions Read the following story. Use the questions on the side to guide your reading. Then, answer the questions that follow.

The Baseball Queen
by Barbara Swanson

I am in bed, and the sun is still shining. **1** I have to go to bed when it isn't even dark!

It isn't dark. It isn't quiet. It isn't night. It isn't fair.

The sun is shining right in my eyes. Who could sleep? Everyone else is outside playing baseball.

I can see them. I can hear them. I wish I were with them.

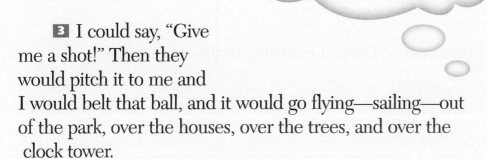

I wish I could get in that game. They're not really bigger than me. I could play ball with them.

3 I could say, "Give me a shot!" Then they would pitch it to me and I would belt that ball, and it would go flying—sailing—out of the park, over the houses, over the trees, and over the clock tower.

The ladies who hold up the clock would try to catch it, but it would be too high for them and much too fast.

It would fly all the way to the Baseball Queen, who catches all the home run balls and keeps them in her Home Run Hall of Fame palace in the sky.

Guided Questions

1 What can you tell about the girl by the way she is thinking?

2 What can you tell about the girl from looking at this picture?

3 Read this paragraph. What does the girl do to pass the time?

She would say, "Who hit this ball?"
Hank Aaron would say, "It wasn't me."
Ted Williams would say, "Not me!"
Mickey Mantle would say, "I didn't hit it!"
Even Reggie Jackson would say, "Don't look at me!"

4 Then, the Baseball Queen would say, "Who is this new Sultan of Swat?" And she would come all the way down to our field.

When she found out that it was me, that I was the one who hit that amazing home run, she would look at me and say, "Why are you wearing your pajamas?"

5 And when the Baseball Queen found out that the greatest home run hitter in the history of baseball had to go to bed before it was even dark, she would march right up to my front door, ring my doorbell, and tell my mother a thing or two.

That's what would happen, if I could only get on that field. If I could only get outside. If I could only stay up. If I could only . . . If I . . .

Guided Questions

4 What does the girl pretend the Baseball Queen does after the girl catches the home run?

5 What do you think happens at the end of this story?

1. Why does the girl daydream? Do you ever daydream when you go to bed?

_____

- -

_____

_____

- -

_____

2. What title does the Baseball Queen give the girl? What do you think this means?

_____

- -

_____

- -

_____

3. Do you like the girl in this story? Explain why or why not. How do the pictures help you make up your mind?

_____

- -

_____

- -

_____

Apply   **Directions** Read the story below. Then, answer the questions that follow.

A Canary's Song
by Timothy B. Collins

One night while Huey was trying to sleep, his new canary started singing in its cage. *Cheep cheep cheep!*

Huey tossed and turned for almost an hour before he finally fell asleep.

The next morning he asked his new pet, "Why did you keep me awake last night with your singing?"

"It's cold in my cage at night," the canary said. "You have covers on your bed, and I have nothing to keep the chill out of my cage."

That night, before Huey went to bed, he placed one of his dad's shirts over the canary's cage to keep out the night air. All was quiet for a short while, and then the canary started singing again. *Cheep cheep cheep!*

"What's wrong?" Huey asked.

"It's lonely in here," the canary said. "I'm used to having other birds in my cage to keep me company."

The next day, Huey found a mirror and placed it inside the cage with the canary. "There," Huey said. "Now when you feel lonely, just look into the mirror and you will see another bird in there with you." The canary thanked Huey for the mirror. He looked at himself for a long time.

That night, Huey was almost asleep when the canary started singing again. *Cheep cheep cheep!*

"What now?" Huey asked.

"I miss my swing," the canary said. "I used to have a swinging perch to rock myself to sleep."

Huey promised that he would go to the pet store the next day and buy a swinging perch for his pet canary.

The next night, Huey placed the swinging perch in the cage.

"Now you can rock yourself to sleep," Huey said. "And maybe I can get some sleep.

Huey lay in his bed for a while, waiting for the canary to sing. All was quiet. No singing. Huey rolled over. "Finally," he said, "a night of good sleep."

 Measuring Up® to the California Content Standards

Several minutes passed by. Huey rolled back over to his other side. He couldn't sleep. It was too quiet.

"Canary bird," Huey said as he sat up in bed.

"Yes?" the canary said.

"I can't sleep," Huey said. "Could you sing me a lullaby?"

"I would love it," the canary said.

The canary started singing a soft, sweet song.

Tweet tweet tweet.

Soon Huey was fast asleep.

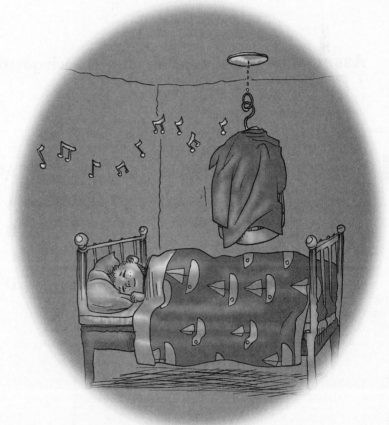

1. Who is the main character?

_____

- -

_____

2. What is Huey's problem?

_____

- -

_____

3. Why can't Harry fall asleep after he puts the swing in the cage? What does he do?

_____

- -

_____

Assessment Practice   **Directions** Answer each question about the stories you just read.

1 **In BOTH stories, a child is**

- **A** outside playing.
- **B** in bed.
- **C** singing songs.
- **D** telling funny stories.

2 **At the end of both stories, a child**

- **A** wakes up.
- **B** goes outside.
- **C** falls asleep.
- **D** plays baseball.

Focus on California Content Standards

| Lesson 21 | Understand Setting |

Standard 2RL3.1   Compare and contrast plots, settings, and characters presented by different authors.

The **setting** is where and when a story takes place. The setting can be a big part of a story. It can affect what characters do or how they behave.

A story can take place anywhere. It can be in a desert. It can be in a forest. It can be deep down in the ocean. It can be far away on another planet.

A story can take place at any time. The time can be today. The time can be tomorrow. The time can be yesterday. It might also be a long, long time ago.

As you read, pay attention to story details. The writer uses details to help you picture the place. Use what you know from your own life. It can help you picture the setting. Read these sentences.

It was a very hot day. The sun was beating down. There was not one sea lion on the rocks. They were all swimming in the cool ocean water.

You know what a hot day feels like. You know what cool water feels like. These details can help you picture the setting of this story.

Think about other stories you have read. How are the settings alike? How are they different?

Directions Read the following story. Use the questions on the side to guide your reading. Then, answer the questions that follow.

Flying Sky
by Nancy E. Walker-Guye

Guided Questions

Kilian shivered. **1** Gray fall clouds flew across the sky. The little stream ran downhill.

Kilian tied a red string to Flying Sky, his blue toy sailboat. **2** The cold wind ripped the string from Kilian's hand. Flying Sky sailed down the stream and disappeared. Wind and tears stung Kilian's eyes.

3 Snow came soon that winter.

4 One morning in early spring, Killian followed the stream downhill. He saw a red string in the melting snow. His heart beating faster, he followed the string to some tall grass.

A small blue boat was stuck in the icy mud. Flying Sky!

5 Kilian stepped closer. His boat was a nest now, with four eggs inside!

Quack! Mother Duck flapped her wings at Kilian.

Kilian smiled and hurried away to tell his friends.

1 Read this sentence and the next. What time of year is it? Where is the setting?

2 What happens to Kilian? Why?

3 What season is it now?

4 What season is it now? What does Kilian do? Why do you think Kilian does this?

5 What has become of Kilian's boat? What is inside?

 Measuring Up® to the California Content Standards

1. How do the clouds move across the sky at the beginning of the story? What kind of day is it?

2. When does Kilian follow the stream downhill? What does he find?

3. Where does he find his boat?

4. Name how many seasons are in this story.

5. Which of the seasons in this story is your favorite? Tell why.

Apply   **Directions** Read the story below. Then, answer the questions that follow.

Sweet Surprises
by Lucy Myers Owens

Rosie looked out the window. It was raining. Actually, it was pouring.

The sky was dark gray, and it was getting darker. The raindrops were huge. Rosie watched them very closely. Every time they hit the top of the birdhouse, they bounced. Rosie groaned. This was the third day in a row of bad storms. There would be no sweet surprises today.

It's summer! It's supposed to be sunny and warm, she thought. Another beach day wasted. She wondered what Cody was doing. Cody was her best buddy. He liked to explore at Blue Duck Beach, too. It was a good place to find treasures!

Rosie thought about last week. Cody had a great find—a piece of deep blue sea glass. It was so pretty. He gave it to Rosie for her collection. After that, they went to James Pond. James Pond was their very favorite place. The pond was right near Blue Duck Beach.

There were two ways to get to James Pond. They could walk through the woods along Pine Tree Path. That's the name Cody gave it. The path went right through a patch of pine trees. At the end was a big dune they had to walk over. Then, they had to take a right and walk down a very narrow path that led to the pond.

They could also walk along Buttercup Path. This path went through a field of buttercups. The path went over a hill. If they took this route, at the top of the hill, they looked right down on James Pond and way out across the sea. On sunny days, it was beautiful, especially if the sky was filled with big white puffy clouds. The white clouds and the blue green sea made Rosie happy. That's why she liked summer best. She liked the color of the sea.

Last week, that's the route they had taken. What a sweet surprise they had. Well, it might not have been so sweet if they'd been closer to the surprise, but they weren't.

It was early in the day. This was always a good time for surprises. It was a bright sunny day. There were a lot of fluffy clouds. The sun was already warm. They had stopped to look at the bug log. They liked bugs. Cody liked spiders. He was poking at the bark. He hoped a daddy longlegs might crawl by. Rosie liked ladybugs. She spent hours looking for them and reading about them. Her biggest bug dream was to find ladybug eggs. If she could find the eggs, she could watch them change into ladybugs. She looked in the garden a lot, but she could never find them.

All of a sudden, Rosie spotted something out of the corner of her eye. It was moving across the path. It wasn't a rabbit! It wasn't a chipmunk! What was it? She looked closely. Then, she grabbed Cody's arm.

"Cody, look!" she whispered.

"Wait a minute, Rosie, I think I found a spider," he said poking the log again.

"Cody, look now, you're not going to believe this!" Rosie whispered.

Cody looked. About five feet away was a mother skunk with her babies. They were crossing the path.

Cody and Rosie stared. The skunks crossed the path and went into some bushes.

"I don't believe it!" said Rosie. "They were sooooo cute!"

"They sure were! I wish that I'd brought my camera!" Cody sighed. "What a picture that would have been! How many people get to see that?"

"Not many!" laughed Rosie. "I guess we can add that to our list of sweet surprises!"

"We sure can!" said Cody. "C'mon, let's go. Let's see if there are any deer tracks at the pond. If there are, we'll come back later. Maybe we can see a baby fawn. Evening is their favorite time at the pond. That would be a sweet surprise, wouldn't it?"

"It sure would!" laughed Rosie as they walked toward the pond.

1. Where is Rosie? What kind of day is it?

_____

- -

_____

2. Read these sentences.

> It was raining. Actually, it was pouring The sky was dark gray, and it was getting darker. The raindrops were huge.

Underline the details that help you picture the day. How do you think Rosie felt?

_____

- -

_____

- -

_____

- -

_____

3. Which path had Rosie and Cody chosen to take to James Pond?

_____

_____

4. What kind of day was it when Rosie and Cody saw the skunks?
Name two details that help you picture that day.

_____

_____

_____

_____

5. What is your favorite kind of day? Where do you like to be? Why?

_____

_____

_____

_____

Assessment Practice   **Directions** Answer each question about the stories you read.

1 **These stories BOTH happen**

A   on very cold days.

B   on sunny days.

C   near bodies of water.

D   in the desert.

2 **Kilian and Rosie BOTH**

A   notice a family of ducks.

B   are tired.

C   hope the sun will come out.

D   see baby animals with their mothers.

Focus on California Content Standards

Lesson 22   **Compare Stories**

Standard 2RL3.3   Compare and contrast different versions of the same story that reflect different cultures.

People like to tell stories. This is true all over the world. Many of these stories are very old. They have been told for a long time. Sometimes, the stories are very much alike. You can find a story about Cinderella. You can find stories like "Jack and the Beanstalk." Stories like this are everywhere in the world.

Stories often tell how or why something happened. A story might tell about how Rabbit got its tail. A story might tell why there are stars in the sky.

There are different kinds of characters in these stories. Sometimes, the main character gets into trouble. The harder she tries to get out of the trouble, the more trouble she gets into. This character can be a boy or a girl. This character can be an animal.

A story can teach people things. It might teach them about how to treat others. It might teach about why music is important.

Sometimes, the main character is a **trickster**. He or she takes many forms. He can be a spider. She can be a rabbit. He can be a wolf. She can live in Africa. He can live in California. She can live in Vietnam.

This character is often very clever. He tries to trick other characters in a story. Sometimes, he gets away with his tricks. Sometimes, he does not.

Directions Read the following story. Use the questions on the side to guide your reading. Then, answer the questions that follow.

How Bluebird Got Her Color

A Pima Indian Tale
retold by Lilly Yellowbird

Guided Questions

Pima Indians live in Arizona. They have lived there for a long time. This is one of their old stories. It has been passed down for many years.

It was a long, long time ago. It was before the animals were different colors. It was before the birds were different colors. It was the time when animals talked.

1 One day Bluebird who was not yet blue sat on a branch. The branch hung out over the lake. She stared at the blue water. **2** She longed to be blue. Blue was her favorite color.

On this day, she chirped a pretty song. This was her song.

> Oh beautiful blue sparkling lake
> I long to be blue.
> Grant me my wish
> And I shall sing for you
> Pretty songs forever!

Then, Bluebird hopped in the lake. She swam and swam and swam. She splashed and splashed and splashed. She chirped and chirped and chirped. She was so happy. Bluebird loved the magic lake.

She played in the lake all morning, but she did not turn blue. Then, Bluebird rested again on the tree branch. She sang her song.

1 Who is the main character?

2 Read this sentence and the next. What does Bluebird want? Why?

Oh beautiful blue sparkling lake
I long to be blue.
Grant me my wish
And I shall sing for you
Pretty songs forever!

Again, she hopped in the lake. She swam. She splashed.
She chirped. It got later and later.

About this time, a coyote walked by. Coyote was very, very
hungry. He spotted Bluebird who still was not blue. He was very
hungry. He listened to her song. He watched her splash. **3** He
waited for her to come out of the water, so he could gobble her
up. She kept swimming. Surely, this bird will get tired of
swimming, Coyote thought. But Bluebird didn't get tired, and it
got later and later.

3 Who is watching
Bluebird? What
does he want?

The evening sun was
getting low. The sky was
streaks of pink and orange.
The sun sat low close to
land. It glowed behind
trees. The world was very
beautiful. **4** Bluebird flew
out of the water. On this
day, her feathers had
turned blue in the magical
lake waters. Coyote forgot
all about his hunger. He
gasped and then spoke softly.

4 What changes
Coyote's mind?

"Bluebird, you are beautiful. You are more beautiful than
the sky. You are more beautiful than the cornflowers in the
meadow. I want to be as beautiful as you. I want to be blue."

"Coyote, you must sing a pretty song," chirped Bluebird.
"As soon as you finish the song, jump in the lake and swim
and swim and swim."

 Measuring Up® to the California Content Standards

"Okay!" said Coyote. He could not wait to turn blue. Bluebird taught Coyote the song.

> *Oh beautiful blue sparkling lake*
> *I long to be blue.*
> *Grant me my wish*
> *And I shall sing for you*
> *Pretty songs forever!*

5 Coyote sang the song, and then he jumped in the lake. He swam and swam and swam. When he climbed out of the lake, he was blue.

5 What happens because Bluebird teaches Coyote her song?

This made Coyote very happy. He jumped up and down. He ran in circles. He thanked Bluebird over and over again. That night he stood in the light of the moon, and he howled. He was quite a handsome coyote, he said to himself. He couldn't wait for the next day so he could show all the animals how beautiful he was.

He got up very early. He started down his favorite path through the field. He looked up at the blue sky. He looked across the field at the cornflowers. He stepped off the path for a drink of cool water at the stream. He looked at himself in the water. I am so handsome, he thought. He turned to walk back onto the path, but Coyote had forgotten about big old willow tree. He smashed right into it. He went flying through the air. He landed in a pile of dirt. Oh no, he thought! When his head stopped spinning, he jumped up. He ran around and around and around. He shook himself. The dirt would not come off.

6 Ever since that time, coyotes have been the color of dirt. It may also be why they howl at the moon. Perhaps they'd still like to be the color blue.

6 What two things does this tale explain about coyotes?

1. What group of people first told this tale?

2. What is the purpose of this tale?

3. Why does Coyote want to be blue?

4. How does Bluebird help him? What happens? Name two details that help you picture that day.

5. What happens to Coyote the next day?

Apply   **Directions** Read the following story. Then, answer the questions that follow.

Lion's Big Party

A folktale from Southern Africa
retold by Salelo Makeba

Long ago, the animals ruled the world. It was in the time of talking animals. Lion was the king. If Lion gave an order, all the animals did what he said. One day Lion gave an order. All the animals in the kingdom must go to his party.

Some of the animals were afraid. They trembled. "Lion plans to eat us," they said, so they didn't go.

But most of the other animals were curious. The party was in the late afternoon. Zebra went and Elephant went too. Rabbit went because he knew the food would be good. Hippo went because he wanted to see Lion's grand house. Donkey went. He told Rabbit that he didn't have anything better to do. Leopard went too.

It was a very fine party. Everyone had a very good time. The animals danced. They sang. They ate good food. There were platters of leaves and berries. There were huge baskets of figs. They drank coconut drinks with mint leaves. They talked and laughed under the palm trees. Lion was pleased.

After a while, Lion let out a huge roar. Everyone got very quiet. Some animals started to shake. They got very worried.

"Listen, my friends, now you can see that I am a good king. I am not as mean as you think I am," he shouted.

He went on, "To show you how kind I am, I have a gift for each of you."

Well, the animals hopped and leaped. They kicked each other. They pushed and shoved. They yelled at each other to get out of the way. They all wanted to get close to Lion. This did not please Lion.

"If you are not polite, you will get NOTHING," he roared.

All the animals stopped at once. They didn't like it when Lion roared, especially Rabbit. It frightened her.

Lion asked who wanted horns. Well, Elephant wanted horns so badly that he shoved everyone out of the way. He grabbed some horns and put them in his mouth. This did not please Lion.

"You greedy elephant," Lion roared. He pulled on Elephant's short nose. Well, he pulled and he pulled. Then, he pulled some more. Elephant's nose got longer and longer. Elephant didn't like his nose, but he didn't say much. This is why Elephant has a very long nose. He still doesn't like it.

Rhino didn't have much better luck. Lion didn't like the way Rhino looked at the horns. Lion hit Rhino right in his face. His horn got all twisted. This is why Rhino's horns look so weird.

Next, Lion gave out ears. They were in a pile, too. He picked up two pairs of very long ears. Donkey and Rabbit were watching quietly. Lion saw them first. He gave them long ears. This is why Donkey and Rabbit have long ears.

Lion saved the best gifts for last. He gave out suits. You can probably figure out that Zebra got a striped suit. Leopard got a spotted suit. Cow and Horse got nice suits, too.

This whole time Giraffe had been watching everything. Lion hadn't even noticed her. Giraffe spoke up. That made Lion angry, so he took away his voice. A few minutes later, Lion noticed that Giraffe looked very sad.

"Oh, Giraffe, don't be sad. I will give you a special suit and special horns," said Lion gently. Giraffe put on his suit and liked it.

Then, Lion decided to give something very special to Giraffe. "Giraffe, I like you a lot. I'm also going to give you a very long neck. A long neck will help you see far away. You will be able to eat the tender leaves at the tops of trees. I will also give you long, long legs. You will be able to run fast." This is why Giraffe has a long neck and long legs.

By now Lion was getting hungry. He didn't want to be bothered anymore. He told the animals to take whatever they wanted. There wasn't much left, but by the end of the party all the horns, ears, and suits were gone.

Lion declared that it had been a very, very good party. Then, he went off to find something to eat.

1. Who is the main character?

_____

- -

_____

2. Why does Lion have the party?

_____

- -

_____

3. What happens when Lion starts to give out gifts?

_____

- -

_____

4. Why does Elephant have a long nose today?

_____

- -

_____

_____

- -

_____

5. What kind of suits did Zebra and Leopard get?

_____

- -

_____

Assessment Practice **Directions** Answer each question about the stories you read.

1 Both stories were FIRST told in the time of

A the blue moon.

B angry elephants.

C magical lakes.

D talking animals.

2 Both stories MOSTLY happen

A at a lake.

B in a big house.

C in the afternoon.

D late at night.

 Measuring Up® to the California Content Standards

Focus on California Content Standards

Lesson 23 **Understand Sound Devices in Poetry**

Standard 2RL3.4 Identify the use of rhythm, rhyme, and alliteration in poetry.

A **poem** is a special kind of writing. It looks special. For example, it has lines. The lines may be long or short. They are like sentences in a story.

A poem also sounds special. It uses words in a special way.

A poem usually has a **rhythm.** Rhythm is the beat you hear when you read a poem. Rhythm makes a poem sound like music. Read these lines aloud. Listen to the beat.

> Red bird, red bird all day long
> Chirps a pretty, pretty song.

You can clap out the rhythm. Clap when you say red. Don't clap when you say bird. Use this pattern for the whole line. Then, use this pattern when you read the second line.

Sometimes the lines **rhyme.** Rhyming words have the same sound at the end. Read these lines.

> Red bird, red bird, way up <u>high</u>
> Always flying in the <u>sky</u>.

<u>High</u> and <u>sky</u> rhyme.

Sometimes writers write words that begin with the same sound together. You can hear the same sound at the beginning of the words. Read this line.

> A <u>crunchy</u> <u>creepy</u> <u>crawly</u> <u>caterpillar</u> <u>crept</u> along the log.

<u>Crunchy</u>, <u>creepy</u>, <u>crawly</u>, <u>caterpillar</u>, and <u>crept</u> begin with same sound.

Guided Reading Instruction

Directions Read the following poem. Use the questions on the side to guide your reading. Then, answer the questions that follow.

The Yak
by Jack Prelutsky

Yickity-yackity, yickity-yak,
1 the yak has a scriffily, scraffily back;
some yaks are brown yaks and some yaks are black,
yickity-yackity, yickity-yak.

2 Sniggildy-snaggildy, sniggildy-snag,
the yak is all covered with shiggildy-shag;
he walks with a ziggildy-ziggildy-zag,
3 sniggildy-snaggildy, sniggildy-snag.

4 Yickity-yackity, yickity-yak,
the yak has a scriffily, scraffily back;
5 some yaks are brown and some yaks are black,
yickity-yackity, yickity yak.

1 Read this line. Underline the two words that have the same beginning sound.

2 Read this line and the next. Circle the words that rhyme. What is another word that rhymes with these two words?

3 What is the beginning sound in all the words in this line?

4 Read this line and the next. Which two words rhyme? What is another word that rhymes with these two words?

5 What color are yaks? Think of a word that rhymes with <u>black</u>.

1. Work with a partner. Take turns. Read this poem aloud. Listen to the beat.

2. Read this line.

> The yak is all covered with shiggildy-<u>shag</u>,

Which two words in this line have the same beginning sound?
What do you think the word <u>shag</u> means?

_____

- -

_____

- -

3. Read this line.

> "He walks with a ziggildy-ziggildy-<u>zag</u>,

Read the words in the box. Circle the words that rhyme with <u>zag</u>.

> snag   flag   snap   zip   nag   stage   tag   brag

4. Read these lines.

> Sniggildy-snaggildy, sniggildy-snag,
> The yak is all covered with shiggildy-shag;
> He walks with a ziggildy-ziggildy-zag,

Underline the word at the end of each line. What do you notice?

_____

- -

_____

5. Why do you think the writer uses so many words that sound alike?

_____

- -

_____

Apply   **Directions** Read the following poem. Then, answer the questions that follow.

Farmyard Wedding
by Joy Cowley

1   At six o'clock in the old hay shed
2   Miss Duck and Mr. Drake were wed.
3   The farmyard creatures smiled and sighed
4   when they saw the lovely groom and bride.

5   Miss Duck wore a frilly dress
6   made from weed and watercress.
7   Mr. Drake looked very neat
8   with pea-pod slippers on his feet.

9   Wise Owl said the marriage words:
10   "Always be happy, quacky birds.
11   Paddle through life side by side.
12   Now the groom may kiss the bride."

13   Then every bird and every beast
14   began the scrumptious wedding feast
15   of turnip puddings and spider pies
16   and corn bread topped with fat blue flies.

17   Miss Frog had baked a wedding cake
18   For Mrs. Duck and Mr. Drake,
19   While Billy Goat had kindly made
20   some ginger beer and lemonade.
21   The Hogwash Band began to play
22   Music for dancing in the hay.
23   The happy couple waddled together,
24   beak to beak and feather to feather.

       Measuring Up® to the California Content Standards

25   The music got faster and Mr. Pig,

26   playing a fiddle and dancing a jig,

27   stuck the fiddle in the bow of his ear

28   and stepped into the ginger beer.

29   Horse then dropped a spider pie

30   that hit Red Rooster in the eye.

31   And Rooster, only half awake,

32   fell into the wedding cake.

33   Soon the swinging Hogwash beat

34   had all the animals on their feet.

35   Rooster boogied with sweet Miss Frog.

36   Chicken jived with Wuffy dog.

37   Mrs. Ewe with all her flock

38   trotted to the Sheepdip Rock,

39   while the happy Duck and Drake

40   tried to do the shimmy-shake.

41   Mrs. Duck said, "Drakey dear,

42   It's time that we were leaving here."

43   Holding wings they crossed the floor

44   And danced right out the hay-shed door.

45   The animals cried, "We'll see you soon.

46   Have a happy honeymoon.

47   May roses grow by your nesting patch,

48   and may all your little ducklings hatch."

49   The bride and groom paddled away,

50   and that was the ending of their wedding day—

51   but not the end of their love and laughter,

52   for they lived happily every after.

1. Read the first two lines. Who got married? How are their names alike?

_____

- -

_____

2. <u>Scrumptious</u> means <u>delicious</u>. <u>Scrump-</u> sounds like <u>lump</u>, and <u>-tious</u> sounds like <u>shess</u>. Say <u>scrumptious</u> a few times. Then, read these lines with a partner. Listen to the beat. Describe it.

> Then every bird and every beast
> began the scrumptious wedding feast
> of turnip puddings and spider pies
> and corn bread topped with fat blue flies.

_____

- -

_____

3. Read these lines.

> The music got faster and Mr. Pig,
> playing fiddle and dancing a jig.

Circle the words in the box that rhyme with Pig and jig.

> fig   fine   sniff   big   twig   sight   dig

4. Read these lines.

> Mrs. Ewe with all her flock
> trotted to the Sheepdip Rock,
> while the happy Duck and Drake
> tried to do the shimmy-shake.

Underline two words in the last line have the same beginning sound?

5. Read these lines.

> Soon the swinging Hogwash beat
> had all the animals on their feet.
> Rooster boogied with sweet Miss Frog.
> Chicken jived with Wuffy Dog.

Which two words rhyme in these lines? Who boogied? Who jived?

Assessment Practice   **Directions** Answer each question about the poem you just read.

1 **Which lines rhyme with each other?**

A 2 and 3
B 14 and 15
C 29 and 30
D 34 and 35

2 **Read this line from the poem.**

| lovely groom and bride |

Which line below has the same rhythm?

A dropped a spider
B creatures smiled and sighed
C stuck the fiddle
D into the wedding

Building Stamina®

Read these two stories. Think about how these stories are the same and how they are different.

That Cat!
by Susan Campbell Bartoletti

Dad poked his hand into my basket. "What's that?" he asked.

"Mew," said the basket.

Dad yanked his hand away. "Oh no," he said. "Not a cat. No way."

I pulled Checkers from the basket. "It's not a cat. It's a kitten. Can I keep him? Please?"

Dad frowned for a minute, thinking. Then he rubbed Checkers under the chin. "You'll have to take good care of him."

I hugged Checkers. "I will," I promised. "He won't be any trouble at all."

And Checkers wasn't—until he grew into a cat.

He wanted to be the first one *in* the house—and the first one *out* of the house.

Sometimes he tripped Dad.

"That cat!" Dad complained.

Checkers climbed onto our roof. He had no trouble getting down. Usually he aimed for Dad.

"That cat!" Dad hollered.

Checkers flushed the toilet and watched the water circle away.

"That cat!" Dad groaned.

Checkers hid in strange places. He liked to surprise people.

One day he hid under the couch. Dad walked by with a glass of orange juice.

Checkers jumped out. He curled around Dad's toes. Orange juice sloshed all over the floor.

Dad hollered and put Checkers outside. "Scram, cat," he said. And he slammed the door.

Dad washed the scratches and peeled open a bandage. He wrapped it around his big toe. He opened four more for his ankle.

I watched from the window. Checkers looked insulted as he walked down the road.

"I'm sorry Checkers scratched you." I said. "He was just playing. He didn't mean to hurt you."

"Don't worry," said Dad. "That cat will be back."

After supper I called for Checkers. But Checkers didn't come.

Nighttime came. I called and called. I banged his food dish with a spoon. But still no Checkers.

I left the porch light on. But the next morning Checkers still wasn't there.

I carried a picture of Checkers to all the neighbors. I drew posters and hung them all over. But nobody found Checkers.

Days went by. Life wasn't the same without that cat.

I was angry with Dad. I didn't think he missed Checkers at all.

Then one night the phone rang. "We'll be right over," said Dad. We drove to a nearby farm. The farmer opened the barn door. Out ran a black-and-white cat.

"Checkers!" I cried. I scooped him up. Checkers purred. We rubbed noses. "I missed you!" I said.

The farmer smiled. "Good thing I saw that ad in the paper."

I looked at Dad. "You put an ad in the paper?"

Dad's face turned red. He nodded.

He petted Checkers. Checkers batted at him with his paw.

Dad laughed. "That cat," he said. "It's good to have him back."

Sam Toes
by Lee Ebler

When Mom said we had to give away Sam Toes, I didn't say a word. I just picked up Sam and walked out to the shed that used to be Dad's workshop.

What Mom said to me wasn't a surprise. I saw it coming.

My name is Nathan. Sam Toes is my cat.

Not long before Dad died, he found Sam behind his store. No one wanted a scruffy kitten, so Dad brought him home. Sam is black, with wise eyes and sharp ears. But all most people notice are his big white toes.

"Meow?"

Sam knows I'm upset.

I wonder if I could explain to Sam about Anna. She's my younger stepsister, and if it weren't for her, I could keep Sam.

But I don't explain, and Sam wiggles to get down. He likes to have adventures in the shed's dusty sunlight.

No one uses the shed now except our elderly neighbors, Mr. Sims and Mr. Irvin. They make wind chimes to sell at the flea market. Dad used to help them.

I grew up loving the sound that filled our shed: hammering, tinkling, laughing sounds. Mom says people love those chimes because their music is mixed with laughter.

I wonder how things are going to change now that I have a stepfather.

"Nathan? Are you in there?"

Through the window, I see my two stepsisters. Rachel is a year older than me. Anna is only five. I wish one of them were a boy. I wish Anna didn't have asthma and animal allergies.

"Don't bring Anna in," I say. "I've got Sam."

 Measuring Up® to the California Content Standards

Last week we had to rush Anna to the emergency room. She couldn't breathe. Mom thinks it was because Sam slept in her room.

"Wait on the step," Rachel says to Anna.

I can't see Anna's face, but her shoulders slump.

"I'm sorry," says Rachel, coming just inside the shed. "About Sam, I mean."

I shrug. Mom asked me earlier who was more important, Sam or Anna. I couldn't answer.

"Isn't there anything we can do?" asks Rachel. We both look at Sam.

Sam is playing with scraps left over from the wind chimes. When he hits metal against metal, it tinkles. Sam is happy.

But I'm not. I don't want to talk. Still, Rachel is trying to help, so I say,

"The ad goes in the paper tomorrow. Sam'll find a good home. Maybe nearby." I try to sound reassuring.

"He might have to move to the North Pole," Anna says sadly from the step. *The Polar Express* is her favorite book.

In my head, I see a crazy picture of Sam standing beside a dogsled, white toes invisible in the snow.

Ann sniffles.

"You ought to take Anna in the house," I say to Rachel. "If she gets upset, she'll start coughing." I'm learning a lot about asthma.

Rachel makes no move. She isn't quite angry, but she looks at me as if I'm missing something.

Anna sniffles louder.

"She's going to cry," I say. I can't understand why Rachel isn't taking care of Anna.

Rachel walks away and starts playing with Sam.

"She's your sister," I say.

"And yours," says Rachel. She's rubbing Sam beneath his chin, and Sam is melting.

I want to say, "Girls!" But I don't. Mom and I talked about *adjustments*.

Then, I remember Anna on the way to the hospital, her face scared and pale. Sam would be OK in a new home, but you can't just send away a little sister.

I guess I know the answer to Mom's question. And I know why Rachel isn't watching Anna.

I need to be a brother.

I sit down next to Anna. "Things will be OK," I say.

"Is Sam mad at me?" asks Anna.

"Sam likes adventures," I say. "If he moves to the North Pole, he might get to ride a dogsled."

Anna considers that.

"But he loves you," she says. I look at Rachel, who is listening. I have a feeling that what I say next will be important.

"Yeah, he does," I say, "and I'll always love him. But when Sam gets a new family, that'll mean more people for him to love."

Isn't our new family working on something like that?

Ping! comes the noise of Sam hitting metal against metal.

"A cat on a sled is funny," says Anna, almost smiling.

"If you'll listen to me," says Rachel, "I don't think we have to send Sam Toes away."

We listen.

In the end, Sam never gets to ride a dogsled, though he still has adventures. Our neighbors Mr. Sims and Mr. Irvin adopted him, so Sam got two homes. I visit him at both. But I like it best when he's brought to the shed.

From my window, I can hear the sounds that go into making the wind chimes. I hear the laughter. And I hear Sam's pleased *meow*.

1 In story 1, why does the father put Checkers outside?

A He puts Checkers outside to get some fresh air.

B He puts Checkers outside because he tripped over him.

C He puts Checkers outside because he is allergic to Checkers.

D He puts Checkers outside so Checkers can climb a tree.

2 In story 2, if Nathan's stepsister had not been allergic to Sam Toes, how would the END of the story be different?

A Nathan would have given away the cat.

B Nathan would have kept his cat at his house.

C Nathan would have given the cat to Mr. Sims and Mr. Irvin.

D Nathan would have given the cat to Rachel.

3 Both stories are about main characters who

A are allergic to cats.

B find cats.

C have cats they love.

D have cats that get lost.

4 In story 2, most of the story takes place inside a

A shed.

B barn.

C school.

D hospital.

5 In story 1, Checkers is found at a

A car wash.

B shelter for animals.

C farm.

D shed.

6 At the END of both stories, the boys are

A   sad.

B   angry.

C   happy.

D   lonely.

7 In story 1, how do you know the father feels badly?

A   He hangs up posters in the neighborhood.

B   He puts an ad in the paper to find Checkers.

C   He drives around looking for Checkers.

D   He gets a new cat for the boy.

8 In story 1, if Checkers had not been full of mischief, how would the story be different?

A   Checkers would have run away.

B   The father would not have put Checkers outside.

C   Checkers would visit the farm.

D   The boy would be angry with his father.

9 Both stories happen

A   in the present time.

B   long ago.

C   on a faraway planet.

D   very late at night.

10 Both stories are about

A   how much fun cats are.

B   problems the main characters have.

C   how to take care of cats.

D   where to find homes for cats.

Watermelon Fever
by Michelle A. Pate

I can't stop thinking about watermelons. Giant watermelons. Juicy watermelons. Wonderful watermelons.

I've saved my money to buy my own. One giant, juicy wonderful watermelon all for me.

Mom says I can't eat the whole chocolate cake by myself because it's bad for me and I'll get sick. But a watermelon? It's fruit. It's good for me.

I'm gonna eat it all up, except for the seeds. Dad jokes that if I eat the seeds, a watermelon will grow inside my stomach. Maybe that wouldn't be so bad . . . . Then, my stomach would be happy all the time!

At the store I look for the biggest, juiciest, the most wonderful one I can find. And there it is, right behind some cantaloupes.

I move the cantaloupes. They're small and light, not like my giant, juicy wonderful watermelon.

"Er . . . omph."

I pick up my watermelon and put it on the floor.

I roll it down the aisle.

"Hey, kid!" a grocery clerk calls out. "What are you doing?"

"I'm rolling my giant, juicy, wonderful watermelon to the checkout line," I tell him.

He walks toward me. "Are you going to pay for it?"

"Of course," I say.

I roll my treasure to the checkout line. The grocery clerk lifts my watermelon for the cashier to weigh. Fifteen pounds! After I pay, the clerk sets it back on the floor for me.

I roll it out the door, then along the sidewalk, three blocks to my house. Sweat drips from my forehead onto the watermelon. I roll it into the kitchen.

"Lucy! What are you doing with that watermelon?" Mom asks.

"I saved up my money and bought it at the grocery store. I'm going to eat it all by myself."

Mom frowns. "You'll get sick," she warns.

"No, I won't. It's fruit. It's good for me," I tell her. "Please?" I beg.

"I've been saving for it."

Mom thinks about it, then smiles as if she knows something. "Okay, but only if you eat it outside," she says.

I roll my giant, juicy, wonderful watermelon out the back door to our picnic table. Mom brings out a knife and some paper plates. My sister follows her.

"Ooh, watermelon," she says. "I want some."

"Sorry," I tell her. "I'm gonna eat it all by myself."

"Mom!" she whines.

"Your sister saved her money and bought it herself. She decides what to do with it."

My brother comes out next.

"Oh, yum, watermelon," he says. "Can I have some?"

"No way," I tell him. "I'm gonna eat this all by myself."

"Mom!" my brother howls.

"It's your sister's watermelon. She decides."

"You can't eat that all by yourself," he challenges.

"Yes, I can!"

Mom cuts the watermelon into four pieces, then cuts each of those in half. Eight pieces total.

I reach for my first piece and take a bite. Red juice runs down my chin.

My father comes out.

"Oh, watermelon!" he says, seeing it.

"Don't even ask," says my brother.

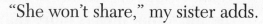

"She won't share," my sister adds.

The four of them stand together around the picnic table watching me.

I eat my second piece. My hands feel sticky, and my face feels wet all over. My belly starts to feel full, but the watermelon tastes so good—I just can't stop eating it.

I bite into my third piece. As I eat, the little mound of black seeds on my plate grows higher.

Five and a half more pieces to go. Red juice dribbles from my chin to my shirt.

I glance up at my family. My sister's mouth is watering. My brother's eyes are locked on the biggest slice left. My parents are watching me in amazement.

I suddenly feel greedy. I'm the only one having fun. "Go ahead," I say. "Have a piece."

Mom smiles. I guess she knew all along that I'd share.

For a second they hesitate, looking at one another to be sure. Then, they storm the picnic table, each grabbing a piece of giant, juicy, wonderful watermelon.

We eat together. Now my whole family has watermelon-red chins, sticky hands, and black seeds piled in front of them. And best of all, everyone is happy.

I decide that giant, juicy, wonderful watermelons are the best. . . . And the only thing better than eating one yourself is sharing it.

1 Who is the main character in this story?

A   mother

B   father

C   Lucy

D   sister

2 Find the word that has the same sound as the underlined letter or letters in the word below.

| ab<u>ou</u>t |

A   door

B   house

C   course

D   Mom

3 Find the word that has been divided into syllables correctly.

A   sud-den-ly

B   sudd-en-ly

C   su-dden-ly

D   sudden-ly

4 What is the correct way to write the word that means more than one family?

A   familys

B   familyies

C   families

D   familyes

5 <u>Checkout</u> is a compound word. You can tell from the two parts of the word that <u>checkout</u> means

A   cash.

B   look closely.

C   a place to pay for what a person buys.

D   the name of a store.

6 This is part of a book's table of contents. Use it to answer the question.

Table of Contents	
Chapter 1: Kinds of Watermelon	4
Chapter 2: Growing Watermelons	6
Chapter 3: Watermelon Tall Tales	10
Chapter 4: Watermelon Recipes	17

If you are reading page 16, which chapter are you reading?

A   Kinds of Watermelon

B   Growing Watermelon

C   Watermelon Tall Tales

D   Watermelon Recipes

7 Where can you buy a watermelon?

A   at a toy store

B   at a shoe store

C   at a magazine store

D   at a food store

8 Why did Lucy buy a watermelon?

A   She wanted to weigh the watermelon.

B   She wanted to make watermelon jam.

C   She wanted to eat the watermelon all by herself.

D   She wanted to give the watermelon to her family.

9 If Lucy had not shared the watermelon with her family, how would the end of the story be different?

A   Lucy would not have learned about sharing.

B   Her family would have told her she was greedy.

C   Her family would have been happy.

D   Lucy would have been happy that she didn't share.

10 In the word <u>wonderful</u>, the -<u>ful</u> means

A   in a certain way.

B   can be.

C   full of.

D   too much.

Chapter 4 Writing Conventions

In chapter 4, you will learn:

- how to identify complete and incomplete sentences;
- how to understand word order;
- how to understand parts of speech;
- how to use commas correctly;
- how to use quotation marks correctly;
- how to use capital letters correctly;

Chapter 5 Writing Strategies and Applications

In chapter 5, you will learn:

- how to write a narrative;
- how to write a friendly letter;
- how to use reference books.

Chapter 4

Writing Conventions

Lesson 24   Identify Complete and Incomplete Sentences

Focus on
California
Content
Standards

Standard 2WC1.1   Distinguish between complete and incomplete sentences.

A **sentence** has a naming part. It tells who or what the sentence is about. We call this part of the sentence the **subject.**

> Maria plays in the park.
> The sun is shining.

A **sentence** also has a telling part. It tells what someone or something does. It can also tell what someone or something is.

> My brother Nick <u>cut his finger</u>.
> The waves <u>are very high</u>.

A **complete sentence** has both a naming part and a telling part. It tells a complete idea.

An **incomplete sentence** is missing one part. It does not tell a complete idea.

Missing the Naming Part:
> Got to school late this morning.

Missing the Telling Part:
> The children in the story.

Guided Writing Instruction

Directions Read the student composition below. Look at how Alicia corrected it. Answer each question in the margin.

Flying a Kite
by Alicia Lowe

1 On Saturday, my mother and father. ^took me to the park^ There was a strong breeze. It was a good day to fly a kite. **2** First, ^we^ tied a tail to the kite. Then we attached a long string. We wound the string around a spool. **3** Next I ^ran^ down the path. The kite caught a breeze. **4** Up, up, and up ^it^ flew. Then it started to dive. **5** ^It landed^ On the ground.

Guided Questions

1 Did Alicia add the naming part or the telling part?

2 Why did Alicia add the word <u>we</u>?

3 What part of this sentence was missing?

4 What part of the sentence is <u>it</u>?

5 Why did Alicia add the words <u>It landed</u>?

Directions Read each item below. Tell whether it is a complete sentence or not a complete sentence. Circle your answer.

1. Ran home from school.   Complete   Not Complete

2. After the movie tonight.   Complete   Not Complete

3. I did all my homework.   Complete   Not Complete

4. Freddie has a kitten.   Complete   Not Complete

5. Owl in the tree.   Complete   Not Complete

Measuring Up® to the California Content Standards

Apply   **Directions** Help Peter fix his composition. Add the missing part to each sentence below. Write the new sentence on the lines.

1. This spring, built a dog house for my puppy Rusty.

_____

- -

_____

2. My friends Sammy and Jack.

_____

- -

_____

3. Got some boards from the lumberyard.

_____

- -

_____

4. Nailed them together.

_____

- -

_____

5. All the while Rusty.

_____

- -

_____

Assessment Practice   **Directions** Answer each question below.

1 **Which of these is NOT a complete sentence?**

A   Read the book last night.

B   The flowers are blooming.

C   After practice, Lamar went home.

D   The dog begged for food.

2 **Which sentence below is missing a part?**

A   The boys wanted a tree house.

B   The books in the library.

C   The lion roared a mighty roar.

D   Chris rode a horse in the park.

Focus on California Content Standards

Lesson 25 Understand Parts of Speech

Standard 2WC1.3 Identify and correctly use various parts of speech, including nouns and verbs, in writing and speaking.

A **noun** names a person, a place, or a thing.

Person	Place	Thing
Maya	park	bicycle
boy	city	key
doctor	hospital	medicine

A **verb** tells what someone or something is doing. It can also tell what someone or something is.

walk	is
run	was
dance	feel

A **pronoun** takes the place of a noun. Remember to write the pronoun I as a capital letter.

I	me
we	us
you	it
he	him
she	her
they	them

An **adjective** describes a noun or pronoun.

<u>large</u> park
<u>busy</u> city
<u>five</u> girls

Nouns, verbs, pronouns, and adjectives are called **parts of speech.**

Guided Writing Instruction

Directions Read the student composition below. Use the questions in the margin to guide your reading.

A City Walk
by Sam Chang

The city is very busy. There are people everywhere. **1**

They
~~People~~ walk to stores. They walk to visit friends. **2** All the
  ^
              are
streets ^ crowded. **3** There are ^many buses in the road. Cars are

                    honk
there, too. **4** The cars ^ their horns. Drivers should be more

polite. Then I would like to walk in the city more. **5** Now

it
~~the city~~ is too noisy.
  ^

Guided Questions

1 What part of speech is the word <u>people</u>? What part of speech is <u>they</u>?

2 Sam had left out a word. What part of speech is <u>are</u>?

3 Sam added the word <u>many</u>. What part of speech is it?

4 Sam added the word <u>honk</u>. What part of speech is it?

5 What part of speech is <u>it</u>?

Directions Read each sentence below. Tell whether the underlined word is a noun, a verb, a pronoun, or an adjective. Write your answer in the blank.

1. Many children <u>play</u> in the park.

_____

2. I like the <u>swings</u> the best.

_____

3. Last night, I saw a <u>beautiful</u> sunset.

_____

4. Please give the book to <u>me</u>.

_____

5. <u>They</u> are having a party.

_____

Apply

Directions Help Lily fix her composition. Add the missing part of speech to each sentence. Write it on the line.

1. Our _____ put on a play.   (Add a noun.)

   _____

   _____

2. _____ played the part of Peter Pan.   (Add a pronoun that shows you played this part.)

   _____

   _____

3. Peter Pan is my _____ character in the whole world.

                                            (Add an adjective.)

   _____

   _____

4. Jorge _____ the part of Captain Hook. (Add a verb.)

   _____

   _____

5. He _____ a pirate's costume.   (Add a verb.)

   _____

   _____

Assessment Practice   **Directions** Answer each question below.

1 **Read this sentence.**

| He hit the ball over the high fence. |

In this sentence, which underlined word is a noun?

A he

B hit

C ball

D high

2 **Read the sentence below.**

| The little puppy barked and then jumped into my lap. |

In this sentence, the word little is

A a noun.

B a pronoun.

C a verb.

D an adjective.

Focus on California Content Standards

Lesson 26   **Understand Word Order**

Standard 2WC1.2   Recognize and use the correct word order in written sentences.

The words in a sentence are arranged so that they make sense. This is called word order. For example, the words below don't make sense. They are out of order.

Red painted Mark color bright a doghouse the.

The sentence below makes sense. The words are in order.

Mark painted the doghouse a bright red color.

A sentence can follow different patterns. Here are some patterns you should know.

Noun/Verb
The dogs / barked.
The people / cheered.

Noun / Verb/ Noun
Jorge / ate / the cereal.
The squirrels / carried/ the nuts.

Noun / Verb / Adjective / Noun
Chris / hit / three / homeruns.
Jenna / ate / a delicious / breakfast.

Noun / Verb / Noun / Noun
Melissa / made / Linda/ a sweater.
Jake / gave / the dog / a bisquit.

Noun /Linking Verb/Adjective

Darren / feels / happy.

The soup / is / cold.

Noun / Linking Verb/ Noun

My brother / is / a soldier.

Mr. and Mrs. Boga / are / our neighbors.

Guided Writing Instruction

Directions Read the student composition below. Look at how Vince corrected it. Answer each question in the margin.

A Water Slide

by Vince Esposito

1 Last weekend, ~~set~~ my parents ^set^ up a waterslide in the backyard. **2** They ~~the slide~~ placed ^the slide^ on a steep hill. **3** The water slide ^was^ long and slippery ~~was~~. My friend Paula came over to play. We walked to the top of the hill. **4** ~~Turns~~ we took ^turns^ going down the hill. Paula went first. She slid all the way to the bottom. Then it was my turn. I slid to the bottom, too. **5** We ~~this~~ did ^this^ over and over again. Then we got tired and stopped. Tomorrow we will play together again. I can't wait. I had so much fun today.

Guided Questions

1 What type of word did Vince move after the noun <u>parents</u>?

2 What type of word did Vince move after the verb <u>placed</u>?

3 What pattern does the changed sentence follow?

4 What type of word did Vince move after the verb <u>took</u>?

5 What type of word is <u>this</u>? What does this type of word do? Where did Vince move it?

Measuring Up® to the California Content Standards

Directions Read each group of words below. Write them in an order that makes sense.

1. Chewed the dog the bone.

2. Martha my friend best is.

3. Gave my teacher a good mark me.

4. Put the flowers my sister Chua in the vase.

5. Brothers the three swimmers good are.

Apply

Directions Help Ginger fix her composition. Put the words in each sentence in an order that makes sense. Write the new sentence on the line.

1. Saw we swans three.

_____

- -

_____

2. Bread crumbs them threw I.

_____

- -

_____

3. The swan up close swam large.

_____

- -

_____

_____

- -

_____

4. Bread crumbs tossed I shore on the.

_____

- -

_____

- -

_____

5. Swan the up came them ate and.

_____

- -

_____

_____

- -

_____

 Measuring Up® to the California Content Standards

Assessment Practice   **Directions** Answer each question below.

1 Read this group of words.

> Stole racoon big the can garbage food the from.

Which item below puts these words in the best order?

A   The big racoon stole food from the garbage can.

B   The racoon big stole food from the garbage can.

C   The big racoon food from the garbage stole can.

D   Sandy to laugh at the silly carton.

2 Which group of words below is NOT in the best order?

A   My sister plays hockey.

B   It is a big tent.

C   The teacher read a story sad.

D   The artist painted my picture.

Focus on California Content Standards

Lesson 27   Use Commas Correctly

Standard 2WC1.3   Use commas in the greeting and closure of a letter and with dates and items in a series.

A **comma** looks like this: , . You use it to separate information. When you read it, you know you should pause slightly.

Use a comma after the greeting in a friendly letter.

> Dear Uncle Jordan,
> Dear Chuck,

Use a comma after the closing words in a friendly letter.

> Best wishes,
> Steven
>
> Your friend,
> Valery

Use a comma between words in a series.

> I have two nickels, three dimes, and a quarter.
> Rex barked, ran for the ball, and caught it.

Guided Writing Instruction

Directions Read the letter below. Look at how Caddie corrected it. Answer each question in the margin.

1519 Main Street

Torrance, CA 90510

September 15, 2005

Guided Questions

1 Dear Aunt Lelia and Uncle Chuck,

Thank you for my birthday present. A book by Laura Ingalls Wilder is just what I wanted. She is my favorite author.

I have already read three of her books. **2** I have read <u>Little House in the Big Woods</u>, <u>Little House on the Prairie</u>, and <u>Farmer Boy</u>. Now I can't wait to read <u>On the Banks of Plum Creek</u>. I will start it tonight.

I have other favorite writers, too. **3** I also like Arnold Lobel, James Marshall, Shel Silverstein, and Beverly Cleary. They make me laugh.

I had another great birthday present. It made me laugh, too. Do you remember my cat Louie? She turned out to be a Louisa. On my birthday, she had kittens **4** We named them Jasper, Twyla, Moonbean, Hermione, Hercules, and Crescent.

Thank you again for the book. I hope you will visit us soon.

5 Best wishes,

Caddie

1 What part of a letter is this? Why did Caddie add a comma?

2 Addie read three books. What do the commas that Caddie added tell you?

3 Caddie added commas. They separate the names of her other favorite writers. How many writers does she name in this sentence?

4 How many commas did Caddie add? How many kittens did Louisa have?

5 What part of a letter is this? Why did Caddie add a comma.

Directions Read each sentence below. Write it on the lines. Add commas where they below.

1. Nick read <u>George and Martha</u> <u>The True Story of the Three Little Pigs</u> and <u>Ramona the Pest</u>.

2. My favorite sports are tennis hockey ice skating and skiing.

3. The boy had some coins a set of keys and three baseball cards in his pocket.

4. Dad made juice from oranges apples bananas and strawberries.

5. Cyndi Linda Jenna Lisa and Skye are all in my troop.

Apply

Directions Help Jacen fix his composition. Add the missing commas. Write the new sentence on the lines.

1. I have five parakeets named Snooky Sleeper Peepers Herman and Nickie.

2. They are bright blue red and yellow.

3. They like to fly around the cage sit on their perches and eat a lot of seeds.

4. I put a swing a plastic tree a food bowl and a water bowl in the cage.

----

5. My friends Craig Barry and Olivia like to watch my parakeets play.

Assessment Practice

Directions Answer each question below.

1 **Read this sentence.**

> Corrie Kevin Lee and Leslie tried out for the team.

What is the correct way to write the sentence above?

A Corrie, Kevin Lee and Leslie tried out for the team.

B Corrie, Kevin, Lee and, Leslie tried out for the team.

C Corrie Kevin, Lee and Leslie, tried out for the team.

D Corrie, Kevin, Lee, and Leslie tried out for the team.

2 **Read this sentence.**

> My puppy's favorite toys are a red ball a rubber bone and an old slipper.

What is the correct way to write the sentence above?

A My puppy's favorite toys are, a red ball, a rubber bone, and an old slipper.

B My puppy's favorite toys are a red ball, a rubber bone, and an old slipper.

C My puppy's favorite toys are a red ball a rubber bone, and an old slipper.

D My puppy's favorite toys are a red, ball, a rubber, bone, and an old, slipper.

Quotations marks look like this " ". They come in pairs.

Quotation marks are important. They show someone's exact words.

Here are three ways to show the exact words.

The words the speaker says come first.

- Put one quotation mark before the words the speaker says.

- Put a comma, an exclamation mark, or a question mark after the words the speaker says.

- Put one quotation mark after the punctuation mark.

- Add the verb and the name of the speaker. This is called the speaker tag.

> "My bicycle is broken," said Jayne.
> "Can you fix it?" Mike asked.

The speaker tag comes first.

- Put a comma after the speaker tag.

- Put one quotation mark before the words the speaker says.

- Put a period, an exclamation mark, or a question mark after the words the speaker says.

- Put one quotation mark after the punctuation mark.

> Barry shouted, "Look at that butterfly!"
> Anita replied, "Where is it?"

The speaker tag breaks up the words the speaker says.

- Put one quotation mark before the words the speaker says.

- Put a comma after the first part of the words the speaker says.

- Put a quotation mark after the comma.

- Add the speaker tag. Put a comma after it.

- Put one quotation mark before the next part of the words the speaker says.

- Put a period, an exclamation mark, or a question mark after the words the speaker says.

- Put one quotation mark after the punctuation mark.

"It's very dark," said Jaime, "and I'm frightened."
"Let's make a camp fire," said Kristin, "and toast some marshmallows."

Measuring Up® to the California Content Standards

**Guided
Writing
Instruction**

Directions Read the story below. Look at how Scott corrected it.
Answer each question in the margin.

A Scary Adventure
by Scott Considine

Jack, Sean, and Alex were sleeping outside. Mom and
Dad had set up a big tent in the yard. **1** "What's that?"
shouted Alex. "I heard a noise."

"I think it's a bear," said Sean. He crawled down deeper
inside his sleeping bag.

2 "Maybe it's Bigfoot," Jack added, "and he is coming to
get us."

They all screamed.

3 Sean said, "I hear him coming closer."

"He's coming to get us," Alex shouted.

4 The three boys huddled together. They shook with fear.

Then Alex pushed open the flap of their tent. It trotted
inside and panted loudly.

"Oh, it's just Buster," said Jack, "our great big shaggy dog."

Guided Questions

1 Look at where Scott
added quotation
marks. What is the
first thing that
Jack shouted?

2 Why did Scott
add a quotation
mark here?

3 Look at where Scott
added quotation
marks. Who is
speaking? What are
his exact words?

4 Why didn't Scott
add quotation
marks here?

5 Who is speaking?
What does he say?

Directions Read each item below. Write it on the lines. Add quotation marks to show what each person says.

1. Did you see that flash of lightning? asked Ginger.

------

2. I have a secret, Mark whispered, but you have to promise not to tell.

------

3. Olivia shouted to the boy crossing the street, Watch out!

------

4. I think it costs five dollars, Stacy guessed.

------

5. I saw that movie, said Jordan, but I didn't like it.

_____

_____

_____

Apply   **Directions** Help Shantelle fix his story. Add quotation marks where they belong. Write each correct sentence on the lines.

1. I bet you can't catch me, said Rabbit.

_____

_____

_____

2. Of course, I can, said Bear.

_____

_____

_____

3. Then Bear boasted, I'm bigger, stronger, and faster than any creature in the forest.

_____

_____

_____

4. Then see if you can keep up, challenged Rabbit. He started to zigzag down the mountain.

_____

- -

_____

- -

_____

5. That's not fair! shouted Bear. I run in a straight line. I can't zigzag back and forth.

_____

- -

_____

- -

_____

Now write the complete story on a separate sheet of paper. Give the story a title.

Assessment Practice

Directions Answer each question below.

1 Which sentence below is written correctly?

A Kumala said, "Don't go near the water!

B Kumala said, Don't go near the water!

C Kumala said, "Don't go near the water!"

D Kumala said, Don't go near the water!"

2 Read this sentence.

I went on the water slide, explained Anne, and then I went in the pool.

What is the correct way to write this sentence?

A "I went on the water slide, explained Anne, and then I went in the pool."

B "I went on the water slide," explained Anne, "and then I went in the pool."

C I went on the water slide, explained Anne, "and then I went in the pool."

D "I went on the water slide," explained Anne, and then I went in the pool."

Focus on California Content Standards

Lesson 29   Use Correct Capitalization

Standard 2WC1.6 Capitalize all proper nouns, words at the beginning of sentences and greetings, months and days of the week, and titles and initials of people.

Capital letters look like this: ABCD. Follow these guidelines for using capital letters.

Capitalize proper nouns. A proper noun names a specific, or special, person, place, or thing.

Common Noun	Proper Noun
girl	Janine
city	San Diego
ocean	Pacific Ocean
holiday	Valentine's Day
planet	Venus

Capitalize words at the beginning of sentences.

The storm ended suddenly. The sky cleared. We saw a rainbow.

Capitalize words at the beginning of greetings.

Dear Sandra,
Dear Uncle Norm,

Capitalize the days of months and days of the week.

January   February   March   April   May   June   July
August   September   October   November   December

Sunday   Monday   Tuesday   Wednesday   Thursday
Friday   Saturday

Capitalize titles of people.

President Bush   Senator Ramos   Mayor Yamoto

Capitalize the first and last word in the title or a book or story, a poem, a movie, a play, a newspaper, or a magazine. Capitalize all other important words.

Digging Up Dinosaurs
News for Kids
In Aunt Lucy's Kitchen
"How to Know the Wild Animals"

Capitalize initials.

U.S.A.   A. P. Stevenson

Guided Writing Instruction

Directions Read the student composition below. Look at how Serena corrected it. Answer each question in the margin.

Night Sights
by Serena Malyana

1 I like to look out over the pacific ocean at night. I listen to the waves as they beat against the shore. **2** I imagine I can see all the way to china. I know I can't, but it is fun to think this. The sky is so black. The stars are so bright. **3** I try to find the big dipper and the little dipper. I look for other special groups of stars, too. **4** Sometimes uncle jordan joins me. We sit together and talk. Sometimes, he recites poems. **5** I really like listening to "the secret of the sea" by henry wadsworth longfellow.

Guided Questions

1 Why did Serena capitalize <u>Pacific Ocean</u>?

2 What word did Serena capitalize? What does it name?

3 Why did Serena capitalize <u>Big Dipper</u> and <u>Little Dipper</u>?

4 What two words did Serena capitalize? Why did she capitalize them?

5 Serena capitalized the name of a poem. Why didn't she put the words <u>of the</u> in capital letters? What other item did she capitalize?

Directions Read each sentence below. Decide which letters should be capitalized. Write the correct sentence on the lines.

1. my parents moved from brooklyn, new york, to san jose, california.

2. cara likes to read poems by maya angelou and langston hughes.

3. roald dahl wrote a very funny book called <u>charlie and the chocolate factory</u>.

4. aunt marie writes for the <u>daily telegraph</u>.

5. last night, mayor jackson visited cliffside children's hospital.

_____

_____

_____

Apply   **Directions** Help Ricardo fix his composition. Read each sentence. Decide which words should be capitalized. Write the correct sentence on the lines.

1. yesterday, senator collins came to our school.

_____

_____

_____

2. she read a poem called "dreams" and talked about all the things we could be in the future.

_____

_____

_____

3. melinda said that she wanted to be an astronaut and fly to mars and venus.

_____

_____

_____

4. i said that my dream was to paint just like my favorite artist frieda kahlo.

_____

_____

_____

5. my best friend kevin said that he wanted to travel to far-off places like asia, africa, and australia.

_____

_____

_____

Assessment Practice

Directions Answer each question below.

1 **Read this sentence.**

> jared and luke saw many tall trees in the jedediah smith redwoods state park

What is the correct way to write this sentence?

A Jared and Luke saw many tall trees in the jedediah smith redwoods state park.

B Jared and luke saw many tall trees in the Jedediah smith redwoods state park.

C Jared and Luke saw many tall trees in the Jedediah Smith Redwoods State Park.

D Jared and Luke saw many Tall Trees in the jedediah smith redwoods state park.

2 **Read this sentence.**

> We celebrate the Fourth of July every year with a big Parade.

Which word should NOT be capitalized?

A We

B Fourth

C July

D Parade

Focus on California Content Standards

Standard 2WC1.7   Spell frequently used, irregular words correctly (e.g., <u>was</u>, <u>were</u>, <u>said</u>, <u>says</u>, <u>who</u>, <u>what</u>, <u>why</u>.)

Standard 2WC1.8   Spell basic short-vowel, long-vowel, r-controlled, and consonant-blend patterns correctly.

Learn the spelling of irregular words.

Some verbs are irregular. Their parts do not follow regular patterns.

Most verbs form their past tense by adding -<u>ed</u>. The verb <u>say</u> is different. Its past tense is <u>said</u>.

Jenna **said,** "Let's go!"

The verb <u>to be</u> is irregular. Look at how the present tense and the past tense are spelled.

Present Tense	**Past Tense**
I **am** strong.	I **was** happy.
He **is** big.	She **was** laughing.
They **are** neighbors.	You **were** cheerful.

Learn to spell words with silent letters.

who   s**c**ene   com**b**   cas**t**le

Learn the spelling of words that begin which the /hw/ sound.

The letters wh can spell the /hw/ sound. They can be tricky. The letters are in the opposite order of the sound.

who   **wh**at   **wh**y   **wh**ich

Learn to spell words with long vowels.

Here are some ways to spell long vowels.

/ā/	/ē/	/ī/	/ō/	/yōo/
make	we	find	no	use
main	street	try	coat	few
play	beat	pie	row	value
they	funny	buy	toe	
	niece			

Learn to spell words with short vowels.

Here are some ways to spell short vowels.

/a/	/e/	/i/	/o/	/u/
cat	set	bit	not	bug
	head		cough	blood
	friend			rough

Some words follow the pattern consonant-vowel-consonant.

A silent <u>e</u> at the end makes the vowel long.

Short Vowel: mad   **Short Vowel:** rat
Long Vowel: made   **Long Vowel:** rate

Short Vowel: bit   **Short Vowel:** not
Long Vowel: bite   **Long Vowel:** note

Be careful when you spell a word with a vowel followed by <u>r</u>.

The letter <u>r</u> may make the vowel sound a little different.

car   perk   mirror   sore   urge

   Measuring Up® to the California Content Standards

Spell every letter in a blended sound.

Two or three consonants may form a blended sound. Write each letter that makes up the sound when you spell it.

drip   **str**eet   **sw**im   **fl**ag   **cl**ue

du**nk**   he**lp**   sou**nd**   **gr**ou**nd**   **sh**ack

Guided Writing Instruction

Directions Read the student composition below. Look at how Ravi corrected it. Answer each question in the margin.

A Fun Game
by Ravi Kumar

1 Scott and I like to play ~~nights~~ ^knights^ and dragons. It is a fun

game. **2** First we ~~bild~~ ^build^ a ~~casle~~ ^castle^. We make it out of cardboard.

3 We paint it ~~brite~~ ^bright^ colers. Then we make costumes. Scott

likes to pretend he is the dragon. He roars very loudly. **4** We

make ~~beleve~~ ^belileve^ he ~~brethes~~ ^breathes^ fire. I have a cardboard sword. **5** I

~~sley~~ ^slay^ the dragon. Then the game is over.

Guided Questions

1 What letter did Ravi add. Why is it difficult to remember to include this letter?

2 What two errors did Ravi make at first?

3 Circle the two misspelled words. How should they be spelled?

4 Look at how Ravi corrected the words in this sentence. What sound do the letters <u>ie</u> spell in <u>believe</u>? What sound do the letters <u>ea</u> spell in <u>breathes</u>?

5 Circle the word Ravi corrected. How should the long /a/ sound be spelled? What is another word that sounds this way and is spelled this way?

Directions Continue reading Ravi's story. Each sentence has one misspelled word. Correct it. Write the corrected sentence on the lines.

1. Sometimes mi sister wants to play.

2. "Let me be the princess," she sez.

3. She weers one of my mother's old long dresses.

4. She sits on a big chair she calls her trone.

 Measuring Up® to the California Content Standards

5. "Now I em the ruler and you are my subjects," she claims.

Apply

Directions Help Alana fix her composition. Each sentence contains two spelling errors. Fix these errors. Write the correct sentence on the lines.

1. My farther is a fire fighta.

2. My grandmother waz a docter.

3. Thay both lik to help people.

4. Dad saves foks hwo are trapped in a burning house.

----

5. Grandma heeled people who wer sick.

Assessment Practice **Directions** Answer each question below.

1 **Read this sentence.**

> Sari <u>throws</u> the <u>ball</u> to the <u>boy</u> in left <u>feild</u>.

Which underlined word is NOT correct?

A throws

B ball

C boy

D feild

2 **In which sentence is the underlined word NOT spelled correctly?**

A <u>Hwich</u> book are you reading?

B How do you make rice <u>pudding</u>?

C Do I need a <u>coat</u>?

D <u>Who</u> wants an apple?

Building Stamina®

The following questions are not about a passage. Read and answer each question.

1 **Which of these is NOT a complete sentence?**

A The butterflies in the bush.

B Jake saw a robin.

C They made a booklet about birds.

D The cat curled up on my lap.

2 **Read this sentence.**

> Jessie fed crickets to the frog.

Which underlined word is a verb?

A Jessie

B fed

C crickets

D frog

3 **Read this sentence.**

> Sam asked, May I pet your dog?

What is the correct way to write the sentence above?

A Sam asked, "May I pet your dog?"

B Sam asked, "May I pet your dog?

C "Sam asked, May I pet your dog?"

D Sam asked, May I pet your dog?"

4 **Read this sentence.**

> We saw snails ants worms and ladybugs in the garden.

What is the correct way to write the sentence above?

A We saw, snails ants worms and ladybugs, in the garden.

B We saw snails, ants worms, and ladybugs in the garden.

C We, saw snails ants, worms, and ladybugs in the garden.

D We saw snails, ants, worms, and ladybugs in the garden.

5 **Which sentence below is NOT correct?**

A "Do you know where Fred lives?" asked Sean.

B "I made a pizza," bragged Mike, "and I fixed the salad, too."

C "The alarm went off too early, complained Father."

D Cheryl asked, "How many people are coming?"

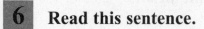

6 **Read this sentence.**

> The <u>tall</u> <u>sunflowers</u> <u>were</u> as <u>high</u> as the fence.

Which underlined word is a noun?

A   tall

B   sunflowers

C   were

D   high

7 **Which sentence below is correct?**

A   I went to the Museum with my Uncle.

B   I sent Rosa a card for Valentine's Day.

C   He read a story called "The sky is Falling."

D   My brother Jake went to Lake tahoe.

8 **Read this sentence.**

> The <u>bus</u> <u>stopped</u> at the corner and <u>weited</u> for the <u>people</u> to get on.

Which underlined word is NOT correct?

A   bus

B   stopped

C   weited

D   people

9 **In which sentence is the underlined word NOT correct?**

A   <u>Which</u> sweater do you want to wear?

B   The coach asked, "<u>Why</u> were you late for practice?

C   Jesse <u>sayed</u>, "I lost one of my gloves."

D   Do you know <u>who</u> is in that movie?

10 **Read this sentence.**

> uncle drake speaks english, spanish, and russian.

What is the best way to correct this sentence?

A   uncle Drake speaks english, spanish, and russian.

B   Uncle drake speaks English, Spanish, and Russian.

C   Uncle Drake speaks English, spanish, and russian.

D   Uncle Drake speaks English, Spanish, and Russian.

Focus on California Content Standards

Standard 2WA2.1	Write brief narratives based on their experiences:
	a. Move through a logical sequence of events.
	b. Describe the setting, characters, objects, and events in detail.
Standard 2WS1.1	Group related ideas and maintain a consistent focus.
Standard 2WS1.2	Create readable documents with legible handwriting.
Standard 2WS1.4	Revise original drafts to improve sequence and provide more descriptive detail.

A **narrative** is a story. The story can be real. It can be make-believe.

The characters can be people. They can be animals.

Every story has a narrator. This is who tells the story. It can be a person or animal in the story. It might be you!

Read these guidelines. They can help you write a story people will like to read.

Guidelines

- **Characters** Characters are the people in a story. They can be animals that talk, too. Who will be in your story? Will you make up a character? Will you write a story about yourself?

- **Plot** The plot is the plan for your story. What is your plan? Think about what happens to the main character. What problem does the character have? How does the character solve the problem?

- **Setting** The setting is where and when the story takes place. Where will your story take place? When will it take place?

• **Details** The details make a story colorful. What details can you tell about the character? What does the character look like? What does the character like to do? What details can you tell about the place? What do you want the reader to see? What do you want the reader to hear or feel?

• **Time Order** What is the order of the events? Think about what happens <u>first</u>. What happens <u>next</u>? What happens <u>last</u>? Use words, such as <u>first</u>, <u>next</u>, <u>then</u>, and <u>last</u> to tell the time order.

Revising and Editing

❏ Is my first sentence interesting? Did I get the reader's attention?

❏ Are the story events in the correct time order? Did I use time order words?

❏ Could I add more details? Are the details colorful?

❏ Have I read over my story several times?

❏ Have I corrected any mistakes? Did I capitalize proper nouns? Did I start each sentence with a capital letter? Did I end each sentence with the correct punctuation? Did I spell each word correctly?

❏ Is my handwriting neat? Will the reader be able to read my writing?

Directions Read the story below. Use the questions on the side to guide your reading.

The Summer of the Glitter Bugs
by Lucy Myers Owens

1 It was July. This meant a month with Gramps on the lake. Gramps was the best. He took them fishing. He taught them how to make birdhouses. He showed them how to catch fireflies.

2 Emma and Nick arrived this afternoon. Gramps was waiting to give them big hugs. Then he sent them upstairs to unpack. They unpacked quickly. After that, they ran down to the dock. They wanted to see how many crayfish were in the trap.

3 It was dark now. They stood on the porch. Grandpa handed them jars with little holes in the tops.

"Gramps, can we keep the firefires?" asked Nick. Nick always wanted to keep the fireflies.

"That wouldn't be fair," Gramps said. "Fireflies like to be with their friends. They don't like jars. Enjoy them for a few minutes. Let them show off for you, then set them free."

4 Emma and Nick ran toward the field. Fireflies were flashing everywhere. Some flashed green. Some flashed orange. Some flashed yellow.

They sat down on their favorite log. Then Emma poked Nicholas and pointed.

"Look," whispered Emma. "The fireflies are really flashing tonight."

Guided Questions
1 Read this sentence and the next. Where and when does this story take place?
2 Who are the main characters?
3 What time of day is it now?
4 Underline the details about the fireflies in this paragraph.

"They are so amazing!" said Nicholas. **5** He tried to catch one. It got away.

5 What is the problem in this story?

"Got one," she screamed. "Wow ! It's flashing orange."

Nick tried to catch another one. It got away. He wasn't having any luck. **6** Emma showed him a trick. After a few tries, he figured out how to catch them.

6 How does Emma help Nick?

Later on, as they walked back to the house, they both agreed it was going to be a very good summer for glitter bugs.

Apply   **Directions** Read the writing prompt below.

> People often help animals. Write a story. Tell about a character who helps an animal with a problem. You can be the main character if you'd like. Explain the problem. Tell how it is solved. Put the events in order. When you are finished, read over your story. Make any changes that you need to.

Before you begin, make a time order chart. Use this sample chart to help you. Think about some ideas for your story. Then write your chart and story on a separate piece of paper.

Time Order Chart

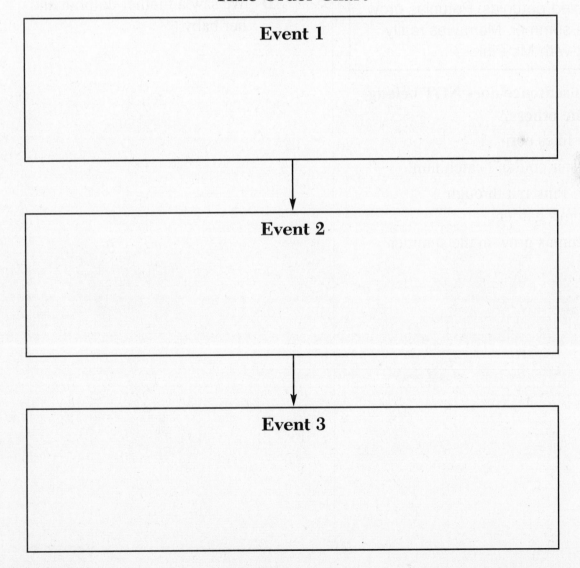

Event 1

↓

Event 2

↓

Event 3

Assessment Practice

Directions Read the following stories. Then answer the questions.

1 Arianna is writing a story about her pet pig. Read the story. Then answer the questions.

> Mr. Pink is a pig. He likes corn. He'll try anything to get out of his pen, so he can get to the cornfield. Well, my brother Buster left the pen gate open. Mr. Pink ran out. Buster couldn't catch him. Mr. Pink ran through Mom's garden. He trampled petunias. Petunias grow in the summer. Mom was really upset with Mr. Pink.

Which sentence does NOT belong with the others?

A He likes corn.

B Buster couldn't catch him.

C Mr. Pink ran through Mom's garden.

D Petunias grow in the summer.

2 Rosalinda is writing a story about whales. She wants to tell about the dolphins she saw on the boat ride. Which sentence BEST tells what the dolphins looked like?

A We saw many dolphins.

B We saw them jump.

C We saw beautiful gray dolphins who jumped and played.

D We saw a mother dolphin and her baby.

Lesson 32   **Write a Friendly Letter**

Standard 2WA2.2	Write a friendly letter complete with the date, salutation, body, closing, and signature.
Standard 2WS1.1	Group related ideas and maintain a consistent focus.
Standard 2WS1.2	Create readable documents with legible handwriting.
Standard 2WS1.4	Revise original drafts to improve sequence and provide more descriptive detail.
Standard 2WC1.4	Use commas in the greeting and closure of a letter with dates and items in a series.

A **letter** is a message you write. One kind of letter is a **friendly** letter. You write friendly letters to people you know. You might write a letter to your cousin. You might write a letter to a pen pal.

It is also fun to receive a friendly letter. If you do, you might want to save it. Then you can read it a lot. It's also very nice to answer the person who wrote you!

Read these guidelines. They can help you write a friendly letter.

Guidelines

- **Choose a Person** To whom would you like to write a letter? Do you have a pen pal? Would you like to tell your cousin some news?

- **Gather Details** Think about what you want to tell the person. Do you want to tell your pen pal that you learned how to swim? Do you want to tell your cousin about the whales you saw?

Use the correct form for a letter.

Date First, you write the date in the upper right-hand corner. The date includes the day, month, and year.

Greeting Start a new line. Write your greeting on the left side of the page. Start your greeting with the word <u>Dear</u> and the person's name. Then write a comma after the person's name. You might also say hello by writing <u>Hi!</u>.

Body of Letter Start a new line below your greeting. In this part of the letter, you write the news or details that you want to share. Make sure that you write clearly.

Closing Start a new line. This is where you say goodbye! Write <u>Love</u> or <u>Your friend</u> on the right side of the page. Then write a comma. If you write two words in your closing, only capitalize the first letter of the first word.

Signature Start a new line under the closing. This is where you write your name. Write your name.

Revising and Editing

Remember, it's important to read over your letter. Correct any mistakes. Ask yourself these questions:

☐ Did I remember to write the date, month, and year? Is the date in the correct place? Did I put a comma between the day and the year?

☐ Did I put a comma after my greeting?

☐ Did I start the body of the letter on a new line?

☐ Did I say what I wanted to say? Did I include interesting details?

☐ Did I start the closing on a new line? Did I put a comma after it?

☐ Did I write my name on a new line?

☐ Have I read over my letter several times?

☐ Have I corrected any mistakes? Did I capitalize proper nouns? Did I start each sentence with a capital letter? Did I end each sentence with the correct punctuation? Did I spell each word correctly?

☐ Is my handwriting neat? Will the reader be able to read my writing?

Guided Reading Instruction

Directions Read the letter below. Use the questions on the side to guide your reading.

Guided Questions

1 August 25, 2005

1 What is the date?

2 Dear Mikayla,

2 To whom is this letter written?

I just got back from the picnic! It was a lot of fun. Aunt Sally said to say hello. She really missed you this year.

Aunt Sally cooked a lot! She made fried chicken. She baked corn bread. She made a big bean salad. The beans were in three different colors.

3 But, the best part was dessert. She baked your favorite coconut cake. She also baked a peach pie. That's my favorite! On top of all that, she made homemade ice cream. The flavors were peach and vanilla. It was sooooooo delicious. I still feel stuffed.

3 Read this paragraph. What does the writer share with Mikayla in this paragraph?

4 After we ate, Aunt Sally helped us make butterfly puddles. I'll show you how when you get back. They're really fun! We also had a relay race with eggs. Sebastian and Dylan won. Cody dropped his egg, and it splattered all over him!

4 What does Aunt Sally help the kids do?

I hope that you are having a really good time. Did you see a bear? Are you swimming every day in the lake? Call me as soon as you get home.

5 Your best friend,
6 Jasmine

5 What words does Jasmine use to close her letter?

6 Who wrote this letter to Mikayla? How do you know?

 Measuring Up® to the California Content Standards

Apply

Directions Read the writing prompt below.

You are away on vacation at the beach. There's a sand sculpture contest. You win first prize. You write a letter to your cousin. You tell her all about what you built. Be sure to write the date, the greeting, and the closing. Don't forget to include some interesting details about how you built your sand sculpture.

Use a separate sheet of paper and use this form to help you write your letter.

_____

_____

_____

_____

_____

_____

_____

_____

_____

Assessment Practice   **Directions** Read the following letter. Then answer the questions.

Zack is writing a letter to his pen pal. Read the letter.
Then answer the questions.

October 18, 2005

Dear Tran,

   Thanks for your letter. I'm very busy today. My block is having a street fair. My best friend James and I are selling lemonade. We're going to make it in a few minutes. Lemonade is delicious, especially when it's hot outside. You said it was hot in Vietnam. You squeeze a lot of fresh lemons. Then you add sugar and water. When you visit next summer, I'll make some for you.

   I was happy to hear about your trip to the city. It must have been fun!

Zack

---

1 **Which would be the BEST sentence to end this letter?**

A I'll send you a picture of a lemon.

B When do you go back to school?

C Write me soon!

D How many holidays do you have this year?

2 **Which sentence below does NOT belong with the others?**

A My friend James and I are selling lemonade.

B You said it was hot in Vietnam.

C You squeeze a lot of lemons.

D Then you add sugar and water.

Focus on California Content Standards

Lesson 33   Understand Reference Books

Standard **2WS1.3**   Understand the purpose of various reference materials (e.g. dictionary, thesaurus, atlas).

When you write a report, you can use reference books. Here are some that are helpful.

A **dictionary** is a book that lists the words of a language and their meanings. The words are listed in ABC order.

When you research information, you might come across a word you don't know. Take the time to look it up in a dictionary. You may also want to check the spelling of a word.

A **thesaurus** is a book that contains synonyms and antonyms. When you write, you might want to change a word. You can look for another word in this book.

An **atlas** is a book of maps. When you write a report about a place, you might want to see where it is on a map.

An **encyclopedia** is a set of books. The books are in ABC order. The books contain articles about many different topics.

Guided Reading Instruction

Directions Read the report below. Use the questions on the side to guide your reading.

The Children's Zoo
by Harry Aroyo

The Children's Zoo is a lot of fun. **1** It is part of the San Diego Zoo. There are a lot of different activities. I visited the zoo on Saturday. I went with my cousins, Sophia and Mireya. **2** First, we saw the brown spider monkeys. They are so cute. Then we visited Bugtown. We saw honeybees. **3** The honeybees were cute. The bees buzzed a lot inside their hive. We also saw giant water bugs. **4** The giant water bugs were creepy. After that, we went to visit Dr. Zoolittle. He is a scientist at the zoo. He showed us how to make maple syrup candy. A long time ago, people used to make this candy. One place people made this candy was in Massachusetts.

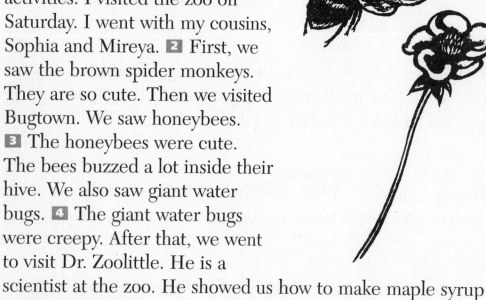

Guided Questions

1 Where could you look to find out where San Diego is?

2 If you wanted to find out more about brown spider monkeys, where would be a good place to look? Why?

3 The writer has already used the word <u>cute</u>. Where could you look to find a word that means about the same as <u>cute</u>?

4 Underline the word <u>creepy</u>. If you didn't know the meaning of this word, where could you look to find out?

 Measuring Up® to the California Content Standards

Apply

Directions Read the writing prompt below. Make a word web like the sample below. You can use reference books to help you write your answer.

> Choose a place you like to visit. It can be anywhere. You can also write about a place you want to visit. Write a report. Tell where it is. Include some interesting details and facts. When you are finished, read over your report. Make sure that you have spelled all the words correctly. Try to use different words to make your report interesting. Make any changes that you need to.

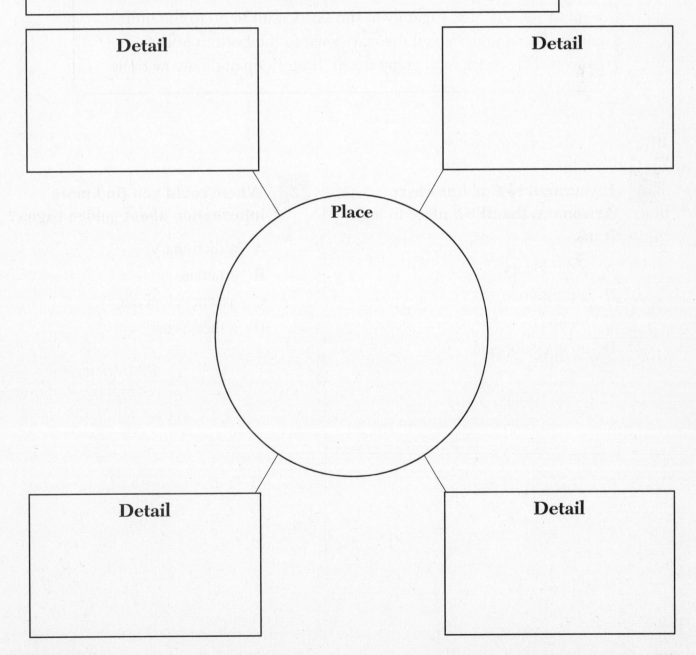

Detail

Detail

Place

Detail

Detail

Assessment Practice   **Directions** Read the following report. Then answer the questions.

The Grand Canyon

by Chan Luong

I want to visit the Grand Canyon. It is in Arizona. There are three things I want to do. I want to go on a walk, so I can find fossils. I want to see a golden eagle fly in the sky. I want to go to the mule corral. These mules go all the way down to the bottom of the canyon. They work hard going down those steep and narrow trails.

---

1 If you want to find out where Arizona is, the BEST place to look is in

   A a dictionary.

   B a thesaurus.

   C an atlas.

   D an encyclopedia.

2 Where could you find more information about golden eagles?

   A a dictionary

   B an atlas

   C an encyclopedia

   D a thesaurus

Cody is writing a story about a robot. Read the story. Then answer the questions.

> Rufus Robot doesn't know what to do. It's a big problem. He is supposed to be gray. But he's really turning red. Rufus eats candy all day long. Fireballs are his favorite. This is how Rufus gets them. He snaps his tin fingers. A fireball drops into his hand. Rufus stays under the fireball tree all day long. He just snaps, snaps, snaps! Sometimes, he has a gumdrop! The fireballs just drop, drop, drop! He just eats, eats, eats!

1 Which sentence does NOT belong with the others?

A This is how Rufus gets one.

B He snaps his tin fingers.

C A fireball drops into his hand.

D Sometimes, he has a gumdrop!

2 Which sentence would be more fun to open the story?

A Rufus is turning red!

B Rufus is a gray robot.

C Rufus can't talk.

D Rufus sends signals.

3 Olivia is writing a story about squirrels. She wants to tell what the squirrel looked like when it ate the peanut. Which sentence BEST tells what the squirrel looked like?

A The squirrel lives in the park.

B It runs right up to people in the park.

C It climbs trees and sits on park benches.

D It sat right up on its hind legs and chewed that peanut up.

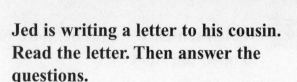

Jed is writing a letter to his cousin. Read the letter. Then answer the questions.

August 5, 2005

Dear Cody,

I got your post card yesterday. Thanks a lot! I can't believe that you saw elephants and lions. I hope that you took a lot of pictures. I really want to see them. Don't forget to bring them with you when you visit.

I hope my parents take me to Africa some day. It must be amazing to see wild animals that close. Did you write Grammy?

Call me next Saturday. I want to hear more about your trip.

Love,
Jed

---

4 **Which sentence does NOT belong with the others?**

A I hope that you took a lot of pictures.

B I hope my parents take me to Africa some day.

C It must be amazing to see animals up close.

D Did you write Grammy?

5 **Which would be the BEST sentence to end this letter?**

A I'll talk to you soon.

B Where are you going next summer?

C Did you go to the beach today?

D I'll send you the book I just read.

6 **Read the sentences below. Which sentence could be added to this letter?**

A Elephants are very big.

B I hope the pictures are good.

C Lions have beautiful manes.

D My brother really likes elephants.

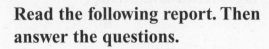
Read the following report. Then answer the questions.

The Starfish
by Lucy Chang

Last summer we visited a big sea aquarium. It is in Long Beach. It took Dad two hours to drive there. When we got there, we went right into the big hall. Right in front of us was a model of a big blue whale. After that, we visited the kelp forest. It was very interesting. I liked seeing all the fish swimming around in the forest.

---

7 **Where could you find more information about blue whales?**

A   a dictionary

B   an atlas

C   a thesaurus

D   an encyclopedia

8 **If you wanted to find a synonym for big, you should look in**

A   an encyclopedia.

B   an atlas.

C   a dictionary.

D   a thesaurus.

9 **If you don't know the definition of <u>kelp</u>, you should look in**

A   an atlas.

B   a dictionary.

C   an encyclopedia.

D   a thesaurus.

10 **If you wanted to find out where Long Beach is, you should look in**

A   an encyclopedia.

B   a thesaurus.

C   an atlas.

D   a dictionary.

Part 2 Building Stamina®

The following questions are not about a passage. Read and answer each question.

1 Which of these is not a complete sentence?

A Lucy got a new bike for her birthday.

B The rabbit ate a carrot.

C The birds in the park.

D We saw a funny movie yesterday.

2 Read this sentence.

> The <u>squirrel</u> <u>ran</u> across the <u>park bench</u>.

Which underlined word is a verb?

A squirrel

B ran

C park

D bench

3 Read this sentence.

> Hannah bought pencils paper crayons and markers today.

What is the correct way to write the sentence above?

A Hannah bought pencils, paper crayons and markers today.

B Hanna bought pencils, paper crayons and markers today.

C Hanna bought pencils, paper, crayons, and markers today.

D Hannah bought, pencils paper crayons and markers, today.

4 Read this sentence.

> We are going to the beach, said Mandy.

What is the correct way to write the sentence above?

A "We are going to the beach, said Mandy.

B "We are going to the beach, said Mandy."

C We are going to the beach," said Mandy.

D "We are going to the beach," said Mandy.

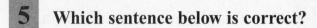

5 **Which sentence below is correct?**

A My Birthday is in july.

B We visited Aunt Lisa at her ranch last Saturday.

C Enrico wants to buy isabella a present.

D My favorite book is "Elf owl's secret."

6 **In which sentence is the underlined word NOT correct?**

A They <u>were</u> happy to get home early.

B Billy <u>says</u> that he can't go with us.

C Jeremiah <u>waz</u> happy that his team won.

D Chloe <u>was</u> first in line for the tickets.

7 **Read this sentence.**

"I <u>want</u> to <u>fead</u> the <u>horses</u> some <u>carrots</u>," said Kayla.

Which underlined word is NOT correct?

A want

B fead

C horses

D carrots

8 **Jillian is writing a story about her rabbit. She wants to tell what the rabbit looked like when she first saw him. Which sentence BEST tells what the rabbit looked like?**

A He hopped across the porch.

B He likes to eat clover.

C He was a little ball of fluffy gray fur.

D He likes to sleep in the afternoon.

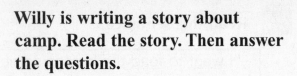

Willy is writing a story about camp. Read the story. Then answer the questions.

We swim every morning. We have different activities in the afternoon. Yesterday we learned how to row. Today we are going on a nature hike. I like to read. Tomorrow we will climb a mountain.

9 **Which sentence does NOT belong with the others?**

A We swim every morning.

B Yesterday we learned how to row.

C Today we are going on a nature hike.

D I like to read.

10 **If you don't know the definition of** <u>nature</u>**, you should look in**

A a dictionary.

B an atlas.

C an encyclopedia.

D a thesaurus.

Glossary

A

abbreviate make a word shorter; p. 22

abbreviation a shortened form of a word, starting with a capital letter and ending with a period; p. 22

adjective a word that describes a noun or pronoun; p. 194

antonym a word that means the opposite of another word; p. 40

atlas a book of maps; p. 243

author's purpose why an author writes something; p. 90

C

cause why something happens; p. 114

character a person, or sometimes an animal, in a story; pp. 148, 231

chart a group of facts about one topic; p. 123

comma a mark used to separate information; p. 204

compound word a big word made up of two smaller words; p. 46

D

data numbers that show information; p. 123

detail information about something; pp. 106, 232

diagram a drawing or picture that shows the parts of something; p. 123

dictionary a book that lists the words of a language and their meanings; p. 243

E

effect what happens because of a cause; p. 114

encyclopedia a set of books with articles about many different topics; p. 243

F

fact a piece of information that is true; p. 106

G

graph a chart that shows information in the form of numbers; p. 123

I

instructions directions that tell you how to do something; p. 130

irregular not following the usual rules; p. 27

L

letter a message you write; p. 237

N

narrative a story; p. 231

noun a word that names a person, a place, or a thing; p. 194

P

parts of speech nouns, verbs, pronouns, and adjectives; p. 194

plot a plan for a story; pp. 141, 231

plural more than one; p. 27

poem a kind of writing that uses words in a special way, sometimes using rhythm and lines that rhyme; p. 171

prefix one or more letters added to the beginning of a root word to change the meaning of the word; p. 56

pronoun a word that takes the place of a noun; p. 194

R

rhyme to have the same sound at the end as another word; p. 171

rhythm the beat that makes a poem sound like music; p. 171

S

setting where and when a story takes place; pp. 155, 231

singular one; p. 27

subject the naming part of a sentence that tells who or what the sentence is about; p. 191

suffix one or more letters that you add at the end of a root word, p. 56

syllable a small part of a word with only one vowel sound; p. 8

synonym a word that means about the same as another word; p.40

T

thesaurus a book that contains synonyms and antonyms; p. 243

traits the qualities of a character in a story; p. 148

V

verb a word that tells what someone or something is doing; p. 194

Acknowledgments

p. 9, "The Thanksgiving Dinner That Almost Wasn't" by Marilyn Kratz, Copyright by Highlights for Children, Inc., Columbus, Ohio; p. 17, "Mr. Bidery's Spidery Garden" by David McCord. Copyright © 1965, 1966 by David McCord. By permission of Little, Brown and Co., Inc.; p. 36, "Ship Shape" by Jennifer Kramer. Reprinted by permission of LADYBUG magazine, April 2005, Vol. 16, No. 8, Copyright © 2005 by Carus Publishing Group; p. 38, "Broccoli Dog" Reprinted by permission of LADYBUG magazine, September 2003, Vol. 15, No. 1, Copyright © 2003 by Lynne Berry; p. 41, "Weather Happens" Reprinted by permission of LADYBUG magazine, April 2005, Vol. 16, No. 8, Copyright © 2005 by Audrey B. Baird; p. 43, "The Ocean is Big, My Father Said" Reprinted by permission of LADYBUG magazine, August 2001, Vol. 12, No. 12, Copyright © 2001 by Linda Ward Stephens; p. B74, "Jazz-Ma-Tazz" Reprinted by permission of SPIDER magazine, November 2000, Vol. 7, No. 11, Copyright © 2000 by Lindy Hansen; p. 106, photos.com; p. 141, "The Rooster and the Fox" by Madeline Juran, Copyright © 2004 by Highlights for Children, Inc., Columbus, Ohio; p. 144, "Skunk Uses Her Head" by Diana C. Conway, Copyright © 2004 by Highlights for Children, Inc., Columbus, Ohio; p. 149, "The Baseball Queen" Reprinted by permission of SPIDER magazine, July 1999, Vol. 6, No. 7, Copyright © 1999 by Barbara Swanson; p. 151, "A Canary's Song" Reprinted by permission of LADYBUG magazine, January 2004, Vol. 15, No. 5, Copyright © 2004 by Timothy B. Collins; p. 156, "Flying Sky" Reprinted by permission of LADYBUG magazine, November 2003, Vol. 15, No. 3, Copyright © 2003 by Nancy E. Walker-Guye; p. 172, "The Yak" from ZOO DOINGS by Jack Prelutsky. Text Copyright © 1983 by Jack Prelutsky. Used by permission of HarperCollins Publishers; p. 174, "Farmyard Wedding" by Joy Crowley, Copyright © 2000 by Highlights for Children, Inc., Columbus, Ohio; p. B178, "The Cat" by Susan Campbell Bartoletti, Copyright © 2005 by Highlights for Children, Inc., Columbus, Ohio; p. B180, "Sam Toes" by Lee Ebler, Copyright © 2003 by Highlights for Children, Inc., Columbus, Ohio; p. B185, "Watermelon Fever" by Michelle A. Pate, Copyright © 2004 by Highlights for Children, Inc., Columbus, Ohio; p. 211, photos.com

Planning Chart

What is my topic?	What should be my writing purpose? ___to entertain ___to describe ___to explain ___to persuade
How long should my writing be?	Who is my audience?

What are three ideas or details I will include in my composition?

a. _____
_____
_____

b. _____
_____
_____

c. _____
_____
_____
_____

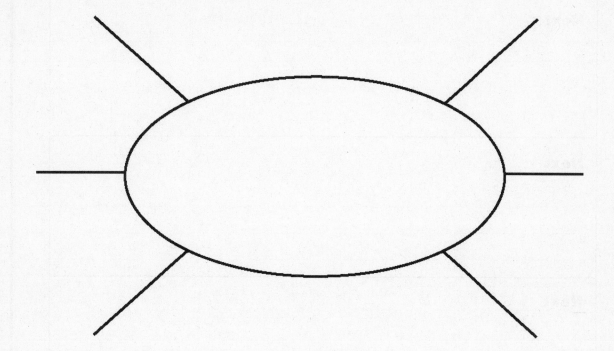

Sequencing List Graphic Organizer

First

Next

Next

Next

Then

Measuring Up® to the California Content Standards

Cause and Effect T-Chart

Cause	Effect

Persuasive Graphic Organizer

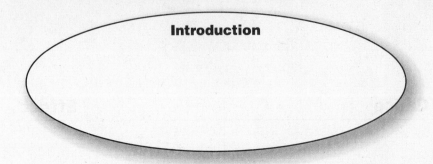

Introduction

Reasons	Supporting Details and Examples

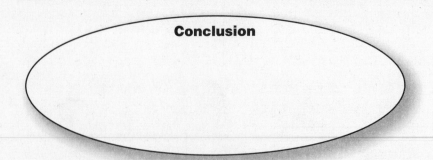

Conclusion